Alfred's

Easy piano so[...]

EASY HITS PIANO EDITION

CW00801474

MOVIE HITS

Produced by
Alfred Music
P.O. Box 10003
Van Nuys, CA 91410-0003
alfred.com

Printed in USA.

ISBN-10: 1-4706-3289-6
ISBN-13: 978-1-4706-3289-2

Cover Photos
Black piano © iStock.com/The AYS

Alfred Cares. Contents printed on environmentally responsible paper.

movie index

contents

ARTHUR'S THEME (BEST THAT YOU CAN DO)

(from *Arthur*)

Words and Music by
BURT BACHARACH, CAROLE BAYER SAGER,
CHRISTOPHER CROSS and PETER ALLEN

Arthur's Theme (Best That You Can Do) - 3 - 1

G
D/F#
G
Cm7
down the town.
just a boy.
Wake up and she's still with
Liv - in' his life one day
F7
Bb
Eb
you,
at a time, he's
e - ven though you left her way a - cross town. You're
show - ing him - self a real - ly good time. He's
Ab
D7
G
D/F#
G
won - der - in' to your - self, hey, what - 've I found?
laugh - in' a - bout the way they want him to be.
cresc.
Chorus:
Cmaj7
Gmaj7
When you get caught be - tween the moon and New York Cit - y,
f

Am7
G/A
Am7
G
I know it's
cra - zy,
but it's true
G/B
Cmaj7
Cmaj7
Bm7
If you get caught be-tween the
road and New York
Cit -
E7sus
E7
Am7
y,
the
best that you can do,
the
best that you can do,
C/G
is fall in love.
1.
D.S.
2.
3.
G
G/B
G
G/B
G
dim.

CAN YOU READ MY MIND?

(Love Theme from *Superman*)

Words by
LESLIE BRICUSSE

Music by
JOHN WILLIAMS

C/B♭ B♭ C/B♭ B♭ B♭/A♭ A♭ B♭/A♭ A♭ Dm7 Em7
look at me quiv-er-ing like a lit-tle girl shiv-er-ing? You can see right
Fmaj7 G7 C D/C
through me. Can you read my mind?
Dm7 F/G G7 C F/G C
Can you pic - ture the things I'm think-ing of? Won - d'ring why you
D/C Fm Gsus G
are all the won - der - ful things you are. You can

Gm7
C7sus
Fmaj7
Gm7
C7sus
fly. You be-long to the sky. You and I could be-long to each
Dm7(♭5)
G7
C
D/C
oth - er. If you need a friend,
Dm7
Em
F
Dm7
G7sus
G7
Cmaj7
Fmaj7
I'm the one to fly to. If you need to be
Cmaj7
Fmaj7
F♯m7(♭5)
Am/B
E
loved, here I am. Read my mind!
rit.

BECAUSE YOU LOVED ME

(Theme from *Up Close and Personal*)

Words and Music by
DIANE WARREN

B♭6
Am7
Dm7
You're the one who held me up,
May - be I don't know that much, but I
nev - er let me fall.
know this much is true,
Fm7
Dm7/G
You're the one who saw me through,
I was blessed be - cause I was
through it all.
loved by you.
You were my
cresc.
Chorus:
C
F
strength when I was weak, you were my
mf
voice when I could - n't speak. You were my
Am7
Gsus
G
eyes when I could - n't see, you saw the
best there was in me, lift - ed me
Em7
Fmaj7
B♭maj7
up when I could - n't reach. You gave me
faith 'coz you be - lieved. I'm

1.
Dm7/G
C
Dm7/G
ev - 'ry - thing I am be - cause you
loved me.
2. You gave me
2.
C
Bridge:
E/G♯
loved me.
You were al - ways there for me, the
Am
E/G♯
ten - der wind that car - ried me. A
light in the dark, shin-ing your love in -
Am7
Dm7
to my life. You've
been my in - spi - ra - tion, through the
C/E
Dm7/G
lies, you were the truth. My
world is a bet - ter place be - cause of

Chorus:
Em7/A
D
G
Bm7
Asus
A
F♯m7
Gmaj7
Cmaj7
Em7/A
D
Em7/A
D
you. You were my
strength when I was weak, you were my
voice when I could-n't speak. You were my
eyes when I could-n't see, you saw the
best there was in me, lift-ed me
up when I could-n't reach. You gave me
faith 'coz you be-lieved. I'm
ev-'ry-thing I am be-cause you
loved me. I'm
ev-'ry-thing I am be-cause you
loved me.
cresc.
f
rit. e dim.

BETTER LOVE

Words and Music by
A. HOZIER-BYRNE

Em/G
F
dis-tant star, The thrill of know-ing how a-lone we are, un-known we
his-to-ry, by those who fig-ure justice in fond mem-o-ry, wit-ness
Am
Em/G
are. To the world and to the both of us,
me. Like fire weep-ing from a ce-dar tree,
F
Am
I con-fessed a long-ing I was dream-ing of some bet-ter love. But there's no
know that my love would burn with me or live e-ter-nal-ly. 'Cus there's no
Chorus:
G
C
F/A
bet-ter love that beck-ons a-bove me, there's no bet-ter love that
f
Am/C
G
1.
E/G#
ev-er has loved me. There's no bet-ter love, so, dar-ling,

F
C
F
feel bet - ter,
feel bet - ter, love.
2.
G
F/A
Am
dar - ling, feel bet-ter, love.
There's no
G
C
F/A
bet - ter love that's
laid be - side me. There's no
bet - ter love that
Am/C
G
E/G♯
jus - ti - fies me. There's no
bet - ter love,
so, dar - ling, dar -
F
C
To Coda
F
ling, feel bet - ter love.
Feel bet - ter love.

Am
G
E/G♯
Feel bet - ter love.
F
C
F
Feel bet - ter love.
C
G
E/G♯
Feel bet - ter love.
D.S 𝄋 al Coda
𝄌 Coda
F
C
'Cus there's no
F
G
Feel bet - ter love.
Am
F/A
Am

EVERGREEN

(Love Theme from *A Star Is Born*)

Words by
PAUL WILLIAMS

Music by
BARBRA STREISAND

Gm7
E♭
C
C7sus
C7
I have found with you.
Like a
F
B♭/C
rose under the A - pril snow,
Gm7
B♭/C
F
C/E
I was al - ways cer - tain love would grow.
Dm
Am7
Love, age - less and ev - er - green,
B♭maj7
A♭maj7
E♭/F
F7
sel - dom seen by two.

B♭maj7
B♭6
Am7
You and I will make each night a first,
mf
B♭maj7
C/B♭
Am7
E♭/F
F7
ev - 'ry day a be - gin - ning.
B♭maj7
E7sus
E7
Am7
A♭
Spir - its rise and their dance is un - re - hearsed.
F/G
G7
B♭/C
They warm and ex - cite us 'cause we have the bright - est
Fmaj7
E♭/F
love, two lights that shine as one,
f

Gm7
B♭/C
F
C/E
morn - ing glo - ry and the mid - night sun.
Dm
Am7
E♭/F
Time, we've learned to sail a - bove; time
B♭maj7
B♭m(maj7)
F
won't change the mean-ing of one love, age - less and
G/F
G♭/F
F
G♭/F
ev - er ev - er - green.
G/F
A♭/F
G/F
G♭/F
F
rit. e dim.
mp

(EVERYTHING I DO) I DO IT FOR YOU

Am
G/B
Am/C
G/B
Am
G/B
tell me it's not worth fight - ing
for.
You can't
tell me it's not worth dy - ing
Am/C
G/D
D
for.
You know it's
true,
ev - 'ry - thing I
do,
I do it for
G
Verse 2:
G
you.
2. Look in - to your heart,
mf
D/G
C
Dsus
D
you will find there's
noth - ing there to
hide.
Take me as I
G
D/G
C
am, take my
life.
I would
give it all, I would

G/D
D
Am
G/B
Am/C
G/B
sac - ri - fice. Don't tell me it's not worth fight-ing for. I can't
Am
G/B
Am/C
G/D
help it there's noth-ing I want more. You know it's true,___ ev-'ry-thing I
D
G
do, I do it for you.
cresc.
There's
Bridge:
F
B♭
F
no love like your love. And no oth - er could give
f
C
G
D
more love. There's no___ way un - less you're there all the

A
D
time, all the way. Oh, you can't
Chorus:
Am
D
Am
tell me it's not worth try - in' for. I can't help it, there's noth - ing I want
D
G
D
more. Yeah, I would fight for you, I'd lie for you, walk the
C
Cm
wire for you, yeah, I'd die for you. You know it's
mp
G/D
Dsus
D
C
G
true, ev - 'ry-thing I do, oh, I do it for you.
rit. e dim.
p

EVERYTHING IS AWESOME
(Awesome Remixxx!!!)
(from *The Lego Movie*)

Lyrics by SHAWN PATTERSON, ANDY SAMBERG, AKIVA SCHAFFER, JORMA TACCONE, JOSHUA BARTHOLOMEW and LISA HARRITON

Music by SHAWN PATTERSON

C
D♭
4
gon-na win for - ev - er. Let's par-ty for-ev - er.
We're the same, I'm like you,
C
you're like me. We're all work - ing in har - mon - y.
Ev - 'ry-thing is
Chorus:
G
D
G
awe - some.
Ev - 'ry-thing is
cool when you're part of a team.
D
C
D
Ev - 'ry-thing is
awe - some
when we're liv - ing our
1.
2.
Em
F
G
dream.
Three, two, one, go.
dream.

FALLING SLOWLY
(from *Once*)

Words and Music by
GLEN HANSARD and
MARKÉTA IRGLOVÁ

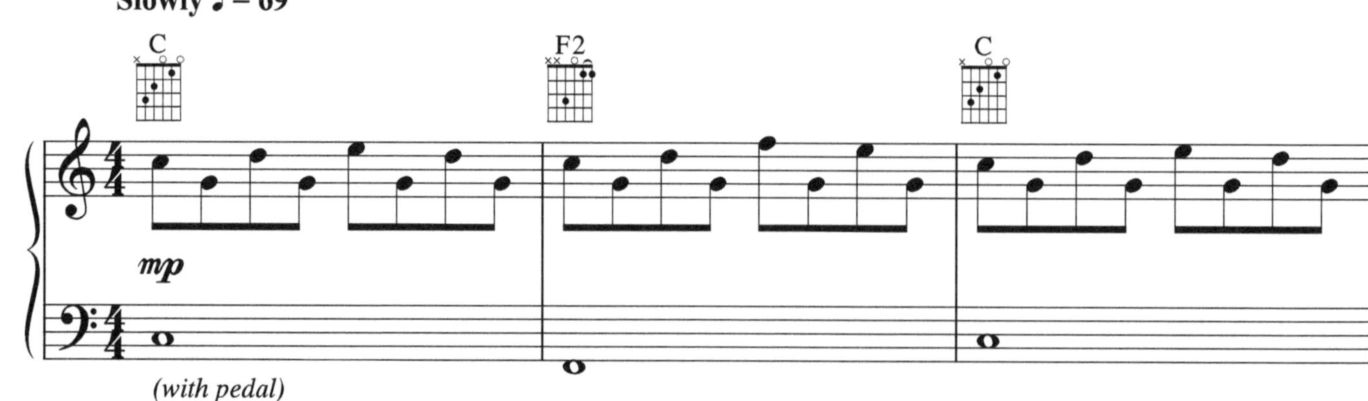

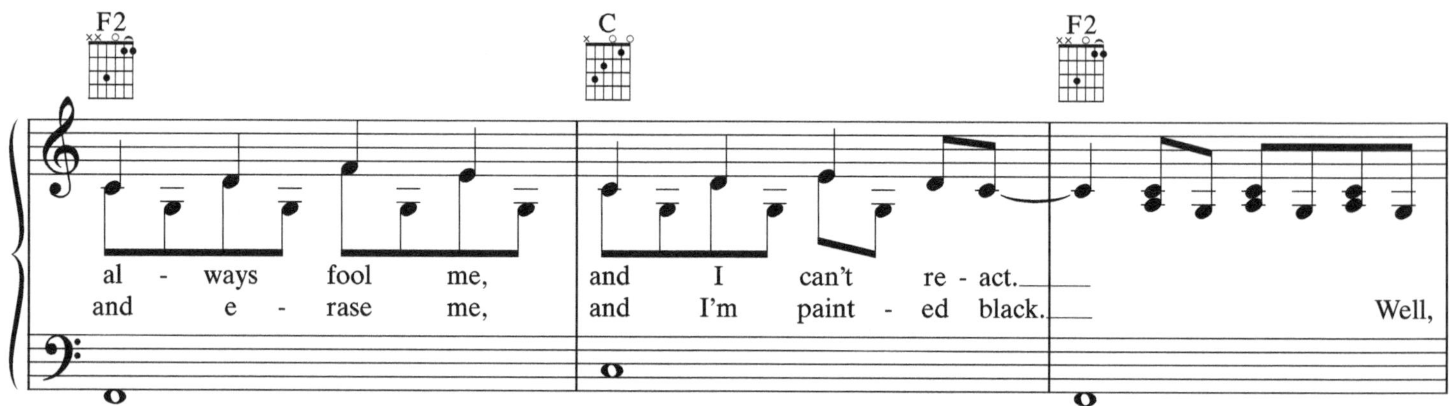

Am
G
Fmaj7
G
Am
G
Games that nev - er a - mount to more than they're meant will play them-selves
you have suf-fered e - nough and warred with your - self. It's time that you
F2
out.
won.
cresc.
Chorus:
C
F2
Am
Take this sink - in' boat and point it home, we've still got
mf
F2
C
F2
time.
Raise your hope - ful voice, you have a

1.
2.
Am
F2
C
choice, you've made it now.
dim.
now.
Fall - in' slow - ly, sing your mel - o - dy, I'll sing it loud.

Fmaj9
C
F2
mp

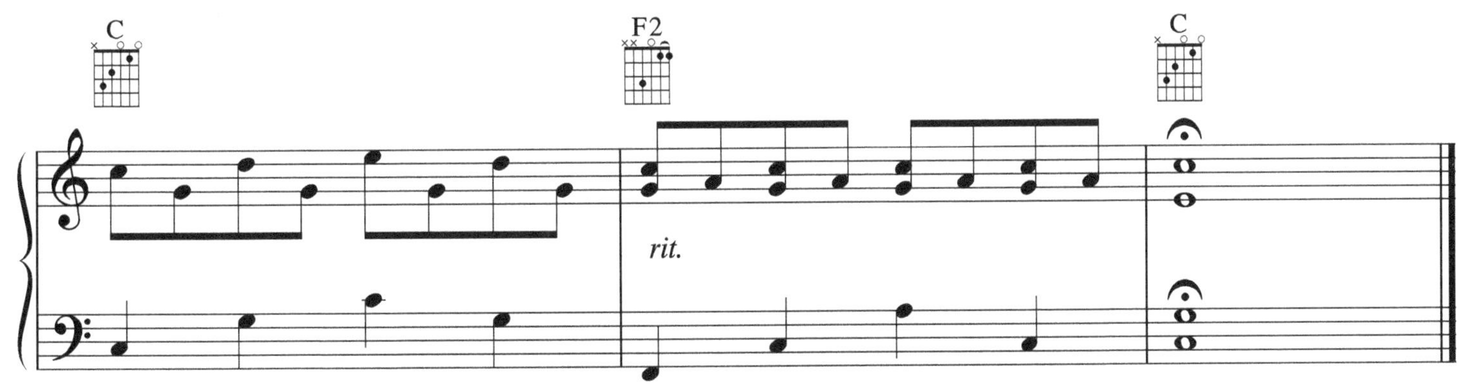
C
F2
C
rit.

FOOTLOOSE

Words by
DEAN PITCHFORD

Music by
KENNY LOGGINS

G
C
I'll hit the ceil - in',
I'm tryin' to tell you
A/C♯
D
Em7
or else I'll tear up this town.
it will if you don't e - ven try.
Fdim7
D/F♯
Chorus:
G
C
To - night I got - ta cut loose, foot -
G
C
G
C
loose; kick off my Sun - day shoes.
2. Ooo

G
C
G
C
1.3. Please, Lou - ise, pull me off of my knees. Jack, get back. Come on be - fore we crack.
wee, Ma - rie, shake it, shake it for me. Whoa, Mi - lo, come on, come on let's go.
C
G
Lose your blues.
Ev - 'ry - bod - y cut foot - loose.
1.
G7
C/G
2.
D.S.
3.
loose. I'm turn - ing it loose.

FOR YOUR EYES ONLY

(from *For Your Eyes Only*)

Lyrics by
MICHAEL LEESON

Music by
BILL CONTI

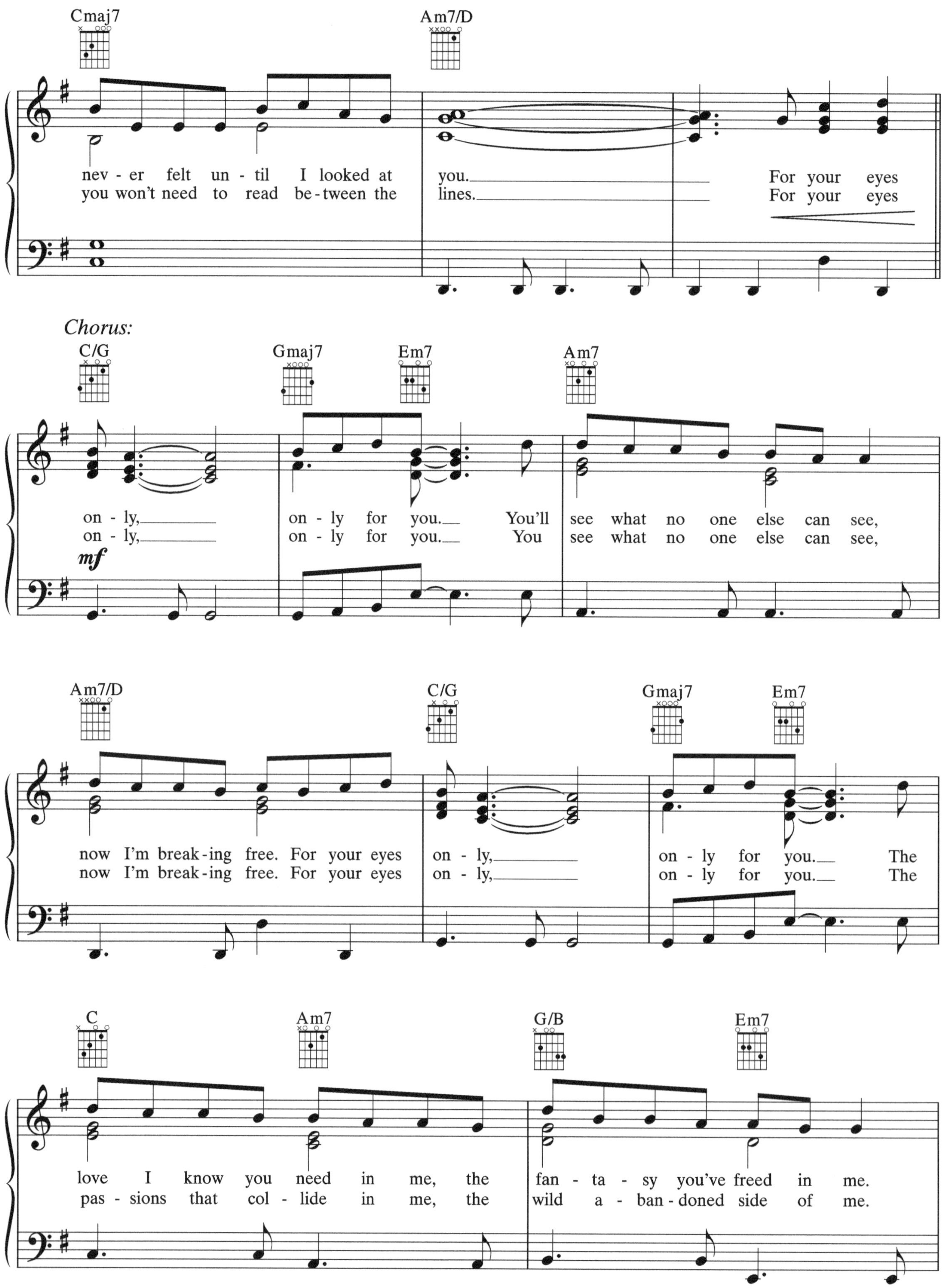
Cmaj7
Am7/D
nev - er felt un - til I looked at you.
you won't need to read be-tween the lines.
For your eyes
For your eyes
Chorus:
C/G
Gmaj7
Em7
Am7
on - ly, on - ly for you. You'll see what no one else can see,
on - ly, on - ly for you. You see what no one else can see,
mf
Am7/D
C/G
Gmaj7
Em7
now I'm break-ing free. For your eyes on - ly, on - ly for you. The
now I'm break-ing free. For your eyes on - ly, on - ly for you. The
C
Am7
G/B
Em7
love I know you need in me, the fan - ta - sy you've freed in me.
pas - sions that col - lide in me, the wild a - ban-doned side of me.

1.
Am7/D
G
On - ly for you,
on - ly for you.
mp
2. For
2.
Am7/D
G
On - ly for you,
for your eyes on - ly.
mp
C/G
G
C/G
G
rit. e dim.

GHOSTBUSTERS

Words and Music by
RAY PARKER, JR.

G F C G F C G F C
Who you gon-na call? Ghost - bust-ers!
There's some-thing weird, and it don't look good.
An in - vis-i-ble man sleep-ing in your bed.
G F C G F C G F C
Who you gon-na call? Ghost - bust-ers!
Bridge:
Gm Gm/F C7/E C7
Gm Gm/F
C7/E C7 G F C

1.
G
F
C
2. If you're
2.
Verse 3:
Who you gon-na call?
Ghost - bust-ers!
3. If you're
all a - lone,
pick
up the phone
and
call
Ghost - bust-ers!
Who you gon-na call?
Ghost - bust-ers!
Bridge:
Gm
Gm/F

C7/E
C7
Gm
3
Gm/F
C7/E
C7
G
F
C
G
F
C
G
F
C
Who you gon-na call? Ghost -
G
F
C
G
F
C
G
F
C
bust-ers!
G
F
C
F
G
Who you gon - na call?
Ghost - bust - ers!

GLORY OF LOVE

(Theme from *The Karate Kid, Part II*)

Words and Music by
DAVID FOSTER, PETER CETERA
and DIANE NINI

Verses 2 & 3:
G
D
2. Some - times I just for - get,
3. You keep me stand - ing tall,
say things I might re - gret,
you help me through it all,
G
C
G/D
D
it breaks my heart to see you
I'm al - ways strong when you're be -
cry - ing.
side me.
G
C/E
F
B♭/D
I don't want to lose you,
I have al - ways need - ed you
I could nev - er make it a -
I could nev - er make it a -
E♭
F/E♭
E♭
F/E♭
lone.
lone.

Chorus:
G
C
G/B
Dsus
D
G
Em7
f I am a man who would fight for your hon - or, I'll be the he - ro you're
Am7
D7sus
D7
Em7
Am7
G/B
B/D♯
dream-ing of. We'll live for - ev - er know-ing to - geth - er that
Em7
Am7
D7sus
D
1.
G
C/E
we had it all for the glo - ry of love.
F(9)
2.
G
C/G
G
Bridge:
Cm
E♭
love. It's like a knight in shin - ing ar - mor,
F
B♭
Cm
E♭
from a long time a - go. Just in time, I will save the day,

Gm
B♭
Cm7
E♭
F
B♭
F/A
C7sus
C7
take you to my cas - tle far a - way.
Chorus:
F
B♭
F/A
Csus
C
F
Dm7
I am a man who would fight for your hon - or,
I'll be the he - ro you're
Gm7
C7sus
C7
Dm7
Gm7
F/A
A/C♯
dream-ing of.
We'll live for - ev - er
know-ing to - geth - er that
Dm7
Gm7
C7sus
C
Dm7
B♭6
we had it all for the
glo - ry of
love.
mp
We did
C
Dm7
B♭6
C
Dm
it all for love.
We did it all for love.

GOLDFINGER

Lyrics by
LESLIE BRICUSSE and
ANTHONY NEWLEY

Music by
JOHN BARRY

Moderately (♩ = 100)

F Db F Db

mf

F Db Cm F

Gold - fin - ger, he's the man, the

Bb E

man with the Mi - das touch, a spi - der's

C F Db

touch. Such a cold fin - ger

Cm
F
B♭
beck - ons you to
en - ter his web of
E
Am
Am(♯5)
sin,
but don't go
in.
Am6
Am(♯5)
Em
Am
B
Gold - en
words he will pour in your
ear,
but his
Em
B7
E
lies can't dis - guise what you
fear.
For a
gold - en girl
Cm
C7
D♭dim7
knows when he's kissed her.
It's the kiss of
death from Mis - ter

F
D♭
Cm
F
Gold - fin - ger.
Pret - ty girl, be -
B♭
E
ware of this heart of
gold.
This heart is
1.
Am
Am(♯5)
Am6
Am(♯5)
cold.
Gold - en
2.
Am
Am(♯5)
cold.
Am6
Am(♯5)
Am
Am(♯5)
Am6
Am(♯5)
He loves on - ly
gold,
on - ly
Am
Am(♯5)
Am6
Am(♯5)
Am6
gold.
He loves
gold.

THE GOOD, THE BAD AND THE UGLY
(Main Title)

Music By
ENNIO MORRICONE

Bm
Em
G
Em
Bm
D
Bm
Em
A
Em
A
Em
A
Em
A
C
Bm
A
G
F♯m
Em
D
C
To Coda
B♭
B
Em

D.S 𝄋 al Coda
𝄌 Coda
Em
A
Em
D
Cmaj7
Bm
Cmaj7
Em
A
Em
A
Em
molto rit.

GONNA FLY NOW
(Theme from *Rocky*)

By BILL CONTI, AYN ROBBINS
and CAROL CONNORS

Modern rock, in two (𝅗𝅥 = 96)

N.C.

mf

Dm7
Em
F
E7sus
Dm7
Cmaj7
Dm7
Cmaj7
Dm7
Em
F

E7sus
Dm7
mf
Em7
Fmaj7
B♭maj7
Asus
E7sus
f

F/G
mf
C/G
Fmaj7
E7sus
f
N.C.

THE GREAT ESCAPE MARCH

Words by
AL STILLMAN

Music by
ELMER BERNSTEIN

1.
2.
A♭
B♭7
E♭
E♭
A♭
E♭
f
Fm
B♭7
E♭
C/G
D/G
C/G
f
F♯
C
F
N.C.
mf

F
B♭
C7
F
B♭
C7
F
B♭
C7
F
B♭
C
F
D
E
A5
A♭
D♭

I LOVE TO SEE YOU SMILE

(from *Parenthood*)

Words and Music by
RANDY NEWMAN

3.
A♭7
E♭7
G7
C7
smile.
Bridge:
F
F♯dim7
C/G
E7/G♯
In the sum - mer, in the spring - time, win - ter or the
A7
D7
fall, the on - ly place_ I'd want to be___ is where
G7
Am7
A♯dim7
G/B
Verse 4:
C
G7(♯5)
I can see___ you smile at me.___ 4. In a world that's full of

C
C7
F
F/A
G7(♯5)
trou - ble,
you make it all worth - while.
F♯dim7
C/G
B♭7
A7
D7
G7
What would I do
if I did-n't have you?
I just love to see you
smile.
I love to see you
smile.
A♭7
E♭7
C6
rit.

THE GREATEST LOVE OF ALL

Words by
LINDA CREED

Music by
MICHAEL MASSER

Em7
Am7
Dm7
F/G
laugh - ter re - mind us how__ we used to
Verse 2:
C
C+
C6
C7
be. 2. Ev - ry - bod - y's search - ing for a he - ro; peo - ple need some - one__ to look__ up to.
F
F+
F6
F+
Em7
Am7
3
I nev - er found an - y - one who ful - filled my needs. A lone - ly place to be, and so I
Bridge:
Dm7
F/G
F
C/E
learned to de - pend on me. I de - cid - ed long a - go__
Dm7
F/G
F
C/E
nev - er to walk in an - y - one's shad - ow. If I fail, if I suc - ceed,__ at

Dm7 F/G F C/E
least I lived as I be - lieve. No mat - ter what they take from me, they
Dm7 F/G
can't take a - way my dig - ni - ty.
Chorus:
Em7 Am7
Be - cause the great - est
mf
Dm7 G G/F Em7 Am7 Dm7 G F6
love of all is hap - pen - ing to me. I found the
Em7 Am7 Dm7 F/G C7sus C C/B♭
great - est love of all in - side of me. The great - est
Am7 Dm7 Gm7 C C/B♭ Am7 Dm7
love of all is eas - y to a - chieve.
f

Gm7
C
C/B♭
Am7
Dm7
Gm7
C7
Learn - ing to love your-self, is the great - est love of
F
G
G/F
Em7
Am7
Dm7
G
G/F
all. And if by chance that spe - cial place that you've been dream - ing
mf
Em7
Am7
Dm7
G
G/F
Em7
Am7
of leads you to a lone - ly place,
Dm7
G7
F
C/E
Dm7
F/G
C
find your strength in love.
mp
rit.

HIGH NOON (DO NOT FORSAKE ME, OH MY DARLIN')

(Main Theme)

Words by
NED WASHINGTON

Music by
DIMITRI TIOMKIN

A
C7
Wait, wait a - long!
F
I do not know what fate a - waits me,
Do not for - sake me, oh my dar - lin'.
F7
B♭
D7
I on - ly know I must be brave.
You made the prom - ise as a bride.
Gm
G♯dim7
F/A
F7
And I must face a man who hates me
Do not for - sake me, oh my dar - lin',
B♭
F
B♭
or lie a cow - ard, a cra - ven
al - tho' you're griev - in', don't think of

F
B♭
F/C
cow - ard,
leav - in'
or lie a
now that I
cow - ard
need you
To Coda
F
in my
by my
grave!
B♭
F
Oh, to be torn twixt love and du - ty, 'spos - in' I lose my fair - haired beau - ty.
B♭
F
Look at that big hand move a - long near - in' high noon.
B♭
F
He made a vow while in state's pris - on, vowed it would by my life or his - 'n.

B♭m
F
F♯dim7
I'm not a - fraid of
death, but, oh,
what will I
Gm7
C7
C+
D.S 𝄋 al Coda
do if you
leave
me?
𝄌 Coda
F
B♭
side!
Wait a - long,
wait a -
F
B♭
long,
wait a - long,
wait a -
F
long!

I DON'T WANT TO MISS A THING

(from *Armageddon*)

Words and Music by
DIANE WARREN

1st time only
F
C/E
Dm7
stay lost in this mo - ment for - ev - er. Ev - 'ry mo-ment
Em7
Fmaj7
Gsus
G
spent with you is a mo-ment I trea - sure.
stay with you in this mo-ment for - ev - er.
Chorus:
C
G/B
Dm7
mf
Don't wan-na close my eyes,
don't wan-na fall a - sleep, 'coz I'd
F
G
C
G/B
miss you, babe, and I don't wan-na miss a thing.
'Coz e-ven when I dream of you,

To Coda
1.
Dm7
F
G
the sweet-est dream would nev - er do. I'd still
miss you, babe, and I don't wan-na miss a thing.
C
G/B
F
mp
2. Lay - ing
2.
miss you, babe, and I don't wan - na miss a thing.
I don't wan - na
Bridge:
B♭
F/A
miss one smile.
I don't wan-na
miss one kiss.
I just wan-na

A♭
E♭/G
be with you, right here with you,
just like this.
I just wan-na
B♭
F/A
hold you close,
feel your heart so
close to mine,
and just
Cm7
Gsus
G
D.S 𝄋 al Coda
stay here in this mo-ment for all the
rest of time.
Ba - by, ba - by.
Coda
F
G
C
G/B
miss you, babe, and I don't wan-na miss a thing.
Dm7
F
G
C
rit.

IF I ONLY HAD A BRAIN

(from *The Wizard of Oz*)

Lyrics by
E.Y. HARBURG

Music by
HAROLD ARLEN

N.C.
F
Dm7
G7
With the thoughts you'd be think - in', you could be an - oth - er Lin-coln if you
C
F/C
C
Gm7
C7
F
on - ly had a brain. Oh, I could tell you
Em7
Am7
Dm7
G7
Cmaj7
why the o - cean's near the shore. I could
Bm7(♭5)
E7
Am
D7/A
think of things I nev - er thunk be - fore, and then I'd sit and think some
G
C
Am7
Dm7
G7
more. I would not be just a nuff - in', my head all full of stuff - in', my

C Csus C Csus C F Dm7
heart all full of pain. I would dance and be mer - ry, life would
G7 C F/C C A7sus A7
be a ding - a - der - ry if I on - ly had a brain. Gosh, it
f
D Bm7 Em7 A7
would be aw - ful pleas - in' to rea - son out the rea - son for
D Dsus D N.C. G Em7
things I can't ex - plain. Then, per - haps I'll de - serve ya and be
A7 D G D A D
e - ven wor - thy erv ya if I on - ly had a brain.
a tempo

INTO THE WEST

(from *The Lord of the Rings: The Return of the King*)

Words and Music by
HOWARD SHORE,
FRAN WALSH and ANNIE LENNOX

Moderately (♩ = 92)

G
Dm
Am
now.
Dream of the ones who came be - fore.
C
G
Dm
They are call - ing from a-cross the dis - tant
Am
Am
C/G
shore.
Why do you weep?
F
G/D
Am
What are these tears up - on your face?
Soon you will see
C/G
F
G/D
all of your fears will pass a - way.

Am
C/G
F
G/D
Safe in my arms,
you're on-ly sleep - ing.
Chorus:
C
F
mf What can you see on the ho - ri - zon?
C
G
Why do the white gulls call?
C
F
A - cross the sea, a pale moon ris - es.
C
G
3
the ships have come to car-ry you home.

Am/E
Em
Dm
G/B
And all will turn to sil - ver glass.
Am/E
C/E
To Coda
F2
G/B
A light on the wa - ter, all souls pass.
Verse 2:
C
G
Dm
mp
2. Hope fades in - to the world of
Am
C
G
night through shad - ows fall - ing
Dm
Am
C
G
out of mem - o - ry and time. Don't say

Dm
Am
C
we have come now to the
end.
White shores are
G
Dm
Am
call - ing.
You and I will meet a -
gain.
And you'll be
Am
C/G
F
G/D
D.S 𝄋 al Coda
here
in my arms
just
sleep - ing.
Coda
F2
G/B
C
grey
ships
pass
in - to the
West.
mp
rit. e dim.
p

I SEE FIRE

Words and Music by
ED SHEERAN

I See Fire - 4 - 1

Verses 2 & 3:
Cm Ab Bb Cm Eb
2. And if we should die to-night, we should
peo-ple fall, then sure-ly
Bb Ab Cm Eb Bb Fm7
all die to-geth-er, raise a glass of wine for the last time. Call-ing
I'll do the same. Con-firmed in moun-tain halls, we got too close to the flame. Call-ing
Cm Eb Bb Abmaj7 Fm7 Gm
out, fa-ther, oh, pre-pare as we will watch the flames burn au-burn on the
out, fa-ther, oh, hold fast and we will watch the flames burn au-burn on the
Ab Fm7 Gm Ab
moun-tain side. Des-o-la-tion comes up-on the sky.
moun-tain side. Des-o-la-tion comes up-on the sky.
Now I see
Chorus:
Cm Ab Bb Cm Ab
fire, in-side the moun-tain. I see fire,
mf

B♭ Cm A♭ B♭ Cm

burn-ing the trees._ And I see fire, hol-low-ing souls._ I see

A♭ *To Coda* 𝄌 B♭ Fm7 1.

fire, blood in the breeze._ And I hope that you'll re-mem-ber me.

Cm A♭ B♭ Cm A♭

B♭ Cm 2.

3. Oh, should my hope that you re-mem-ber me. And if the

Bridge:

Fm7 Cm E♭ B♭ Fm7 Cm

night is burn - ing I will cov - er my eyes._ For if the dark re - turns_ then my

Eb
Bb
Fm7
Cm
Eb
Bb
broth-ers will die. And as the
sky is fall ing down, it crashed in -
to this lone-ly town. And with the
Fm
Gm
Ab
Bb
D.S 𝄋 al Coda
shad-ow up-on the ground, I hear my
peo - ple scream-ing out. Now I see
Coda
Bb
Cm
Ab
Bb
Cm
blood in the breeze. And I see
fire,
in-side the moun-tain. I see
Ab
Bb
Cm
Ab
fire,
burn-ing the trees. And I see
fire,
Bb
Cm
Ab
Bb
Cm
hol-low-ing souls. And I see
fire burn au - burn on the
moun - tain side.
mp

IN DREAMS

(from *The Lord of the Rings: The Fellowship of the Ring*)

Words and Music by
FRAN WALSH and HOWARD SHORE

F G C G/D Am/C G/D Fmaj7 Am/E
hear your name And in dreams, we will
F G Am F C E♭ C A♭/C E♭/B♭
meet a - gain.
mf
mp
G7sus/C A♭ B♭ C E♭ C A♭ B♭
When the
D F♯m G D/F♯ G A D/F♯ A/E
seas and moun-tains fall and we come to end of days, in the
mf
D F♯m G D/F♯ G Bm/F♯ A/E D
dark I hear a call, call-ing me there. I will go there and back a - gain.
rit.
mp

IT MIGHT BE YOU

(Theme from *Tootsie*)

Words by
ALAN and MARILYN BERGMAN

Music by
DAVE GRUSIN

Moderately slow (♩ = 80)

G G/B C C/D

mp

(with pedal)

G G/B C C/D

Verses 1 & 2:

G G/B Bm7 D/C C C/D

1. I've been pass - ing time_ watch-ing trains go by,__ all of my life,_
(2.) look - ing back as lov - ers go walk - ing past,_ all of my life,_

G G/B Bm7 D/C C

ly - ing on the sand_ watch - ing sea - birds fly,__
won - d'ring how they met_ and what makes it last.__

A/C♯
G/B
B7/D♯
wish - ing there would be some - one wait - ing
cresc. If I found the place, would I rec - og -
mf
Chorus:
Em7
A9
Am7
D
home for me.
nize the face?
Some - thing's tell - ing me it might be you.
D/E
Em7
Am7
D
1.
C/D
It's tell - ing me it might be you.
2. All of my life
2.
Bridge:
B7/D♯
B7
Em
D/E
mf
So man - y qui - et walks to take.
Bm7
Dm7
Am
So man - y dreams to wake.
And we've

Cm
G
F#m7
Bm7
so much love to make.
Em7
G/A
A7
Dmaj7
I think we're gon - na need some time. may - be
F/G
G7
Cmaj7
Bm7
Em7
all we need is time.
mf
And it's
Verse 3:
Am7
D
C/D
G
tell - ing me it might be you all of my life.
3. I've been
G/B
Bm7
D/C
C
A/C#
sav - ing love songs and lull - a - bies.
And there's
cresc.

G/B
B7/D♯
Em7
A9
so much more no one's ev - er heard be - fore. Some - thing's
f
Chorus:
Am7
D
D/E
Em7
tell - ing me it might be you. It's tell - ing me it must be you, and I'm
mf
C/D
G
feel - ing it - 'll just be you all of my life. May - be it's you, may - be it's you
C
I've been wait - ing for all of my life. May - be it's you,
may - be it's you I've been wait - ing for all of my life.
rit. e dim.
mp

JAMES BOND THEME

By MONTY NORMAN

Em6 Em Em(♯5)

f *mp*

(with pedal)

Em6 Em(♯5) Em6 Em(♯5) Em6 Em(♯5)

Em Em(♯5) Em6 Em(♯5) Em6 Em(♯5)

mf

Em6 Em(♯5) Em Em(♯5) Em6 Em(♯5)

Em6
Em(♯5)
Em6
Em(♯5)
Em
Em(♯5)
Em6
Em(♯5)
Em6
Em(♯5)
Em6
Em(♯5)
Em
Em(♯5)
Em6
Em(♯5)
Em6
Em(♯5)
Em6
Em(♯5)
Em
Em(♯5)
Em6
Em(♯5)
Em6
Em(♯5)
Em6
Em(♯5)

With a slight swing feel
Em
Em(♯5)
Em6
B9
f

Tempo I
Em6
Em
Em(#5)
Em6
Em(#5)
mf
Em
Em(#5)
Em6
Em(#5)
Em6
Em(#5)
Em6
Em(#5)
Em
Em(#5)
Em6
Em(#5)
Em6
Em(#5)
Em6
Em(#5)
N.C.
Em9(maj7)
mp

LET IT GO

(from Walt Disney's *Frozen*)

Music and Lyrics by
KRISTEN ANDERSON-LOPEZ
and ROBERT LOPEZ

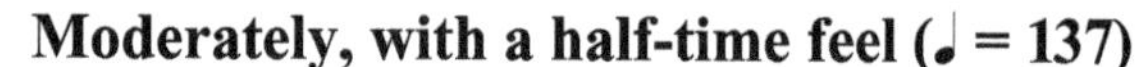

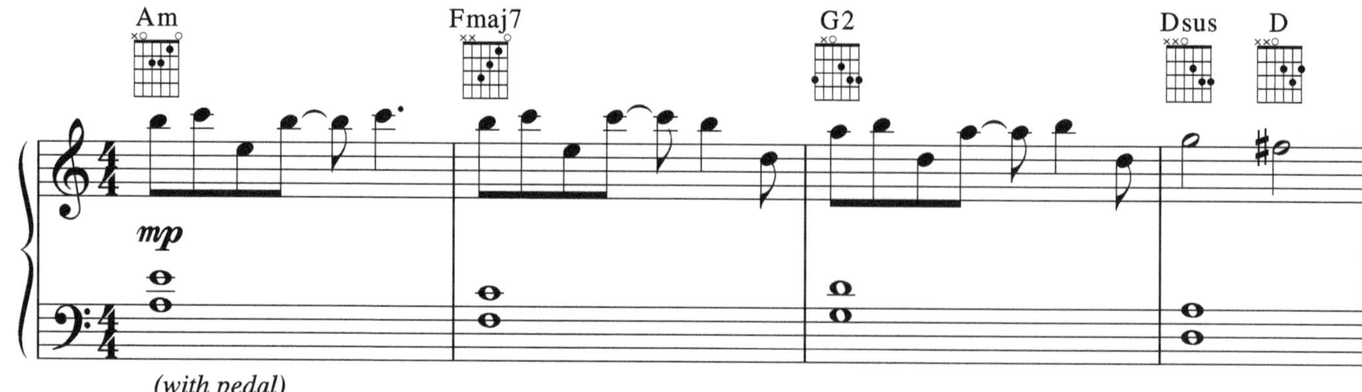

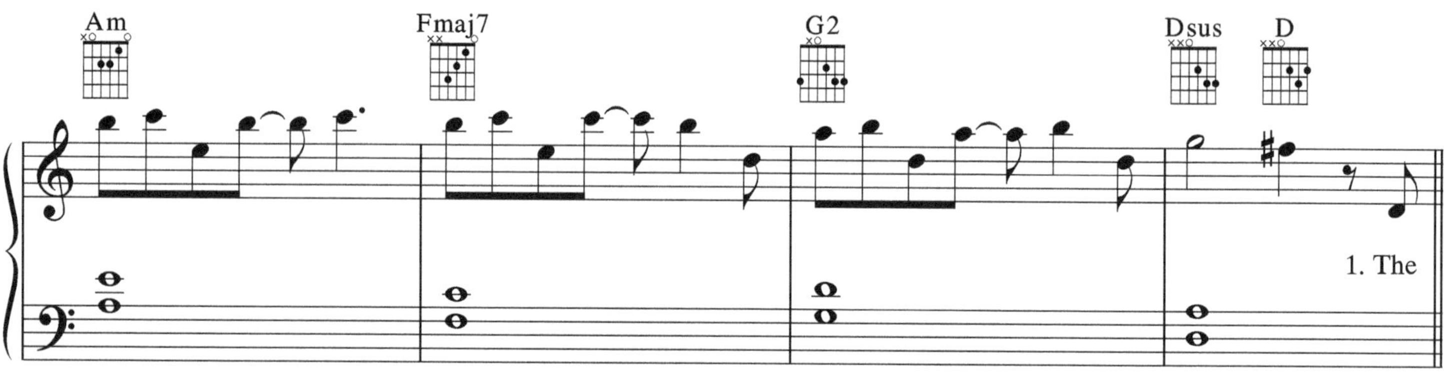

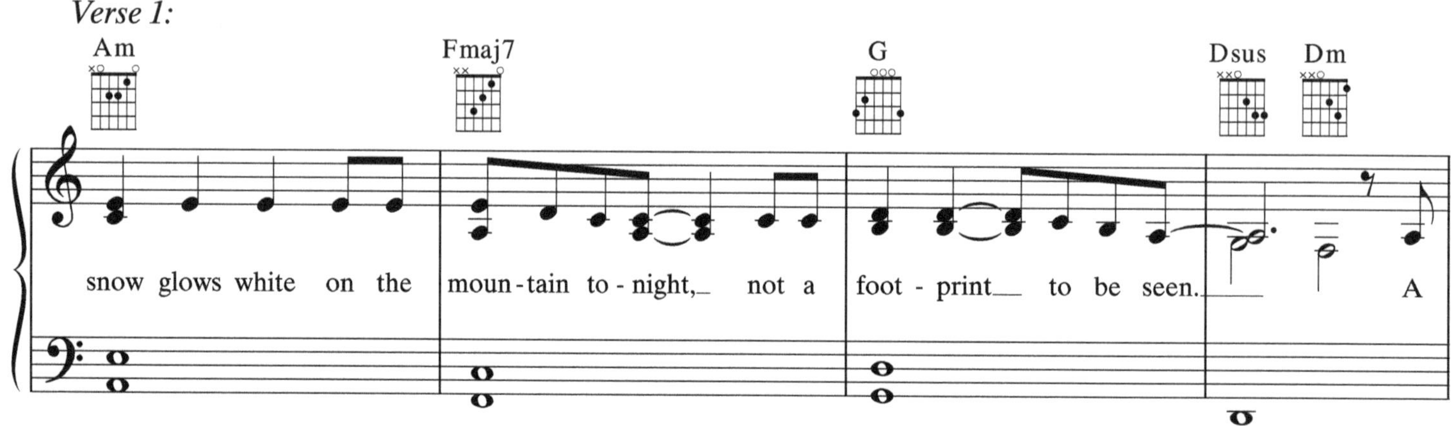

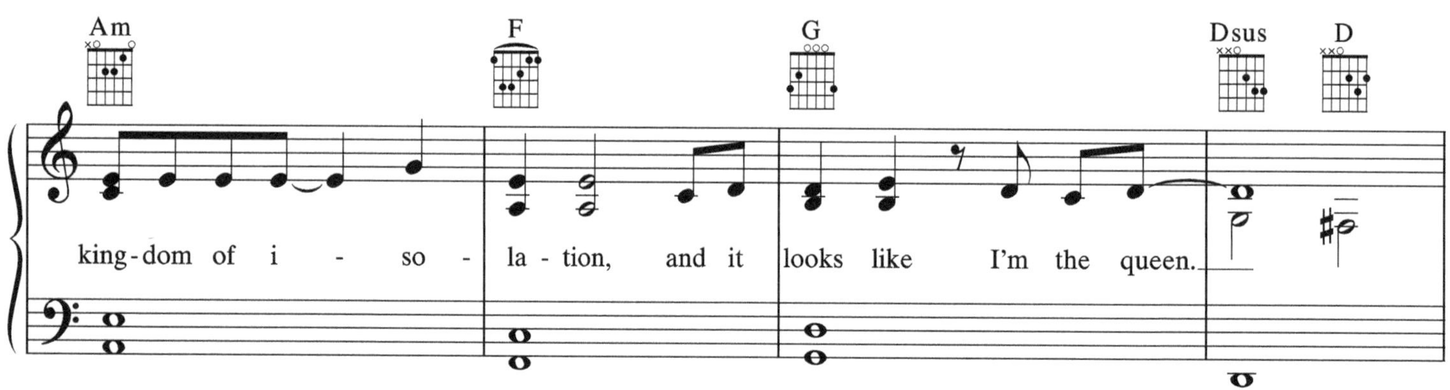

Am
Fmaj7
G
Dsus
Dm
The wind_ is howl-ing like_ this swirl-ing storm in - side.
Am
G
Dsus
D
Could-n't keep it in,_ heav-en knows I've tried._
G
F
mf
Don't let_ them in,_ don't let_ them see. Be the good girl you al-ways have_ to
G
F
be. Con-ceal,_ don't feel,_ don't let_ them know. Well, now_
Chorus:
C
G
_ they know. Let it go,_ let it go._ Can't
f
mp

Am
F
C
G
hold it back an - y - more. let it go, let it go. Turn a - way
Am
F
C
G
and slam the door. I don't care what they're
Am
F
Em
E♭
going to say. Let the storm rage on. The
F
C
G/B
cold nev - er both-ered me an - y - way.
mf
Verse 2:
Am
F
G
Dm
2. It's fun - ny how some dis - tance makes ev - 'ry - thing seem small. And the

Am
G
Dsus
D
fears that once con - trolled me can't get to me at all.
G
F
It's time to see what I can do to test the lim - its and break
G
F
through. No right, no wrong, no rules for me. I'm free.
Chorus:
C
G
Am
Let it go, let it go. I am one with the wind and sky.
let it go. And I'll rise like the break of dawn.
f
To Coda
F
C
G
Am
F
Let it go, let it go. You'll nev - er hear me cry.
Let it go, let it go. That per - fect girl is gone.

C
G
Am
F
Here I stand, and here I'll stay. Let the
Em
E♭
F5
storm rage on.
Bridge:
My pow - er flur - ries through the air
mp
in - to the ground.
My soul is spi - ral - ing in fro -
f
mp
zen frac - tals all a - round.
G
And one thought crys -
f
mp

A
tal - liz - es like an ic - y blast.
I'm nev - er
f
F
G
Dm
F
D.S 𝄋 al Coda
go - ing back, the past is in the past.
Let it go
mf
mp
f
𝄌 Coda
C
G
Am
F
Here I stand in the light of day.
Fm
E
E♭
Let the storm rage on.
F
The cold nev - er both - ered me an - y - way.
mp
p
8va

THE MAGNIFICENT SEVEN

By ELMER BERNSTEIN

F
B♭maj7
C
F
B♭
Dm7
B♭
F
B♭maj7
C
F
E♭
Gm7
E♭
Gm7
B♭/C
C
F
Dm7
Gm7
1.
Am
B♭/C
C
F
B♭maj7
C
F/A
B♭
C
2.
Am
B♭
C
Gmaj7
A
Gmaj7
A
D
Dsus
D

G
C/G
D/G
G
C
f
G
E7/G♯
Am7
Am7/D
G
Em7
Am7
Bm
C/D
D
G
C/G
G
C/G
G
C/G
G
Cmaj7
D
G
Cmaj7
D
G
mp
sfz

MAMMA MIA

Words and Music by
BENNY ANDERSSON,
STIG ANDERSON
and BJORN ULVAEUS

B♭
C
B♭
F
con - trol.
There's a fire with - in my soul.
Just one
C
B♭
F
C
look and I can hear a bell ring.
One more
look and I for - get ev - 'ry - thing,
oh, oh.
Chorus:
F
B♭
E♭/B♭
B♭
mp
Mam-ma Mi - a,
here I go a - gain.
My, my, how
F/B♭
F
can I re - sist ya?
Mam-ma Mi - a,
does it show a - gain,
B♭
E♭/B♭
B♭
F
my, my, just
how much I've missed ya?
Yes, I've been bro -
mf

C/E
Dm
C
ken - heart - ed,
blue since the day we part - ed.
B♭
E♭
B♭
Gm7
C
F
Why, why, did I ev - er let you go?
Ma - ma Mi - a,
Dm
B♭
E♭
B♭
Gm7
1.
C
now I real - ly know,
my, my I should not have let you go.
F
F+
F6
F+
2.
B♭
E♭
B♭
Gm7
C
F
my, my, I should not have let you go.
f

MIDNIGHT COWBOY

Music by
JOHN BARRY

1.
2.
A♭
D♭maj7
G7
C
B♭
mf

NEVER ON SUNDAY

Lyrics by
BILLY TOWNE

Music by
MANOS HADJIDAKIS

C7
Or you can kiss me on a Wednes-day, a Thurs-day, a Fri-day and Sat-ur-day is
And if you make it on a bleak day, a freak day, a week-day, why you can be my
F
best.
guest.
C7
But nev-er, nev-er on a Sun-day, a Sun-day, a
But nev-er, nev-er on a Sun-day, a Sun-day, the
F
Sun-day 'cause that's my day to rest.
one day I need a lit-tle rest.
C7
Most an-y
F
day you can be my
C7
guest,
Gm7
an-y day you say,
C7
but my day of

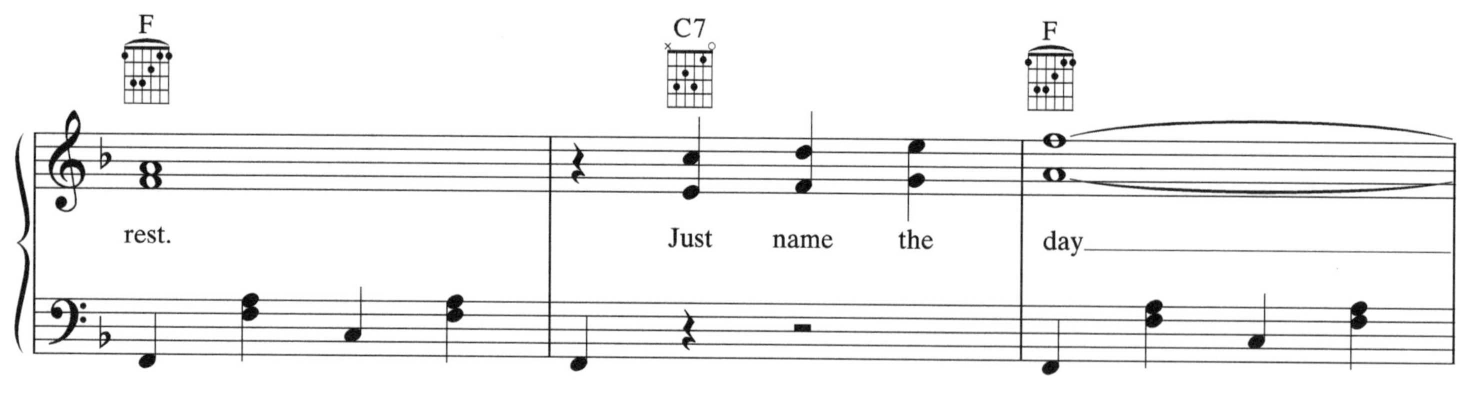
F
C7
F
rest.
Just name the day

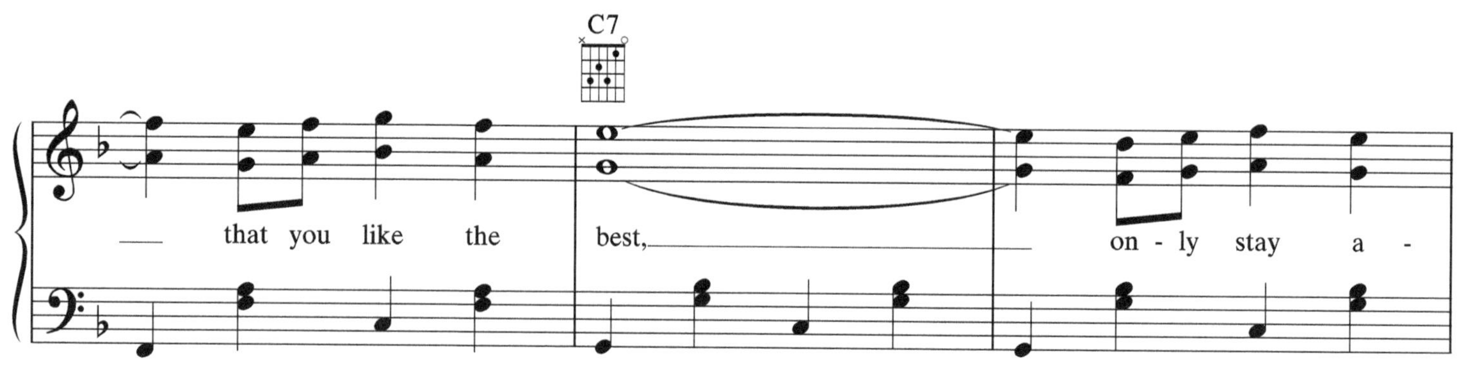
C7
that you like the best,
on - ly stay a -

Gm7
C7
1.
F
way
on my day of rest.

2.
F
2. Oh, you can kiss me on a
rest.

NOBODY DOES IT BETTER

(From *The Spy Who Loved Me*)

Lyrics by
CAROLE BAYER SAGER

Music by
MARVIN HAMLISCH

Bridge:
C
C7/E
F
Fm6
I was - n't look - in' but some - how you found me.
The way that you hold me when - ev - er you hold me.
C
C7/E
D7
D♭7
C
C7/E
I tried to hide from your love - light. Like heav - en a - bove me,
There's some kind of mag - ic in - side you that keeps me from run - nin'.
F
Fm6
E7
A7
D7
G7sus
the spy who loved me is keep - in' all my se - crets safe to -
But just keeps it com - in', how'd you learn to do the things you
1.
2.
C
C
C
C7
night.
do?
3. And

Verse 3:

F
Fm6
C
F
Fm6
no-bod-y does it bet - ter,
makes me feel sad for the
C
F
Fm6
E7
Am
rest.
No-bod - y does it
half as good as you.
Dm7
C/E
F
F♯m7(♭5)
F/G
Ba - by, ba - by,
ba - by, you're the
C
C7
Cdim7
A♭dim7
C
best.
rit.

THE NOTEBOOK

(Main Title)

Written by
AARON ZIGMAN

Bm
C
A♭dim7
Am
Cmaj7/E
F
mf
G7sus
G7(♭9)
C
Fm/A♭
mp
a tempo
C
Fm/A♭
Am
mf
Dm7
G
C sus2 sus4
C
f
F
Dm
G7(♭9)
G7
mf
mp molto rit.

C
Fm/A♭
C
p a tempo
F
G7/B
C
E/B
Am
D7/F♯
mf
G
B7/F♯
Em
Cm/E♭
G/D
D7(♭9)
mp
rit.
G
Cm/G
Gsus2 sus4
G
p a tempo
rit. e dim.
pp

OVER THE RAINBOW

(from *The Wizard of Oz*)

Lyrics by
E.Y. HARBURG

Music by
HAROLD ARLEN

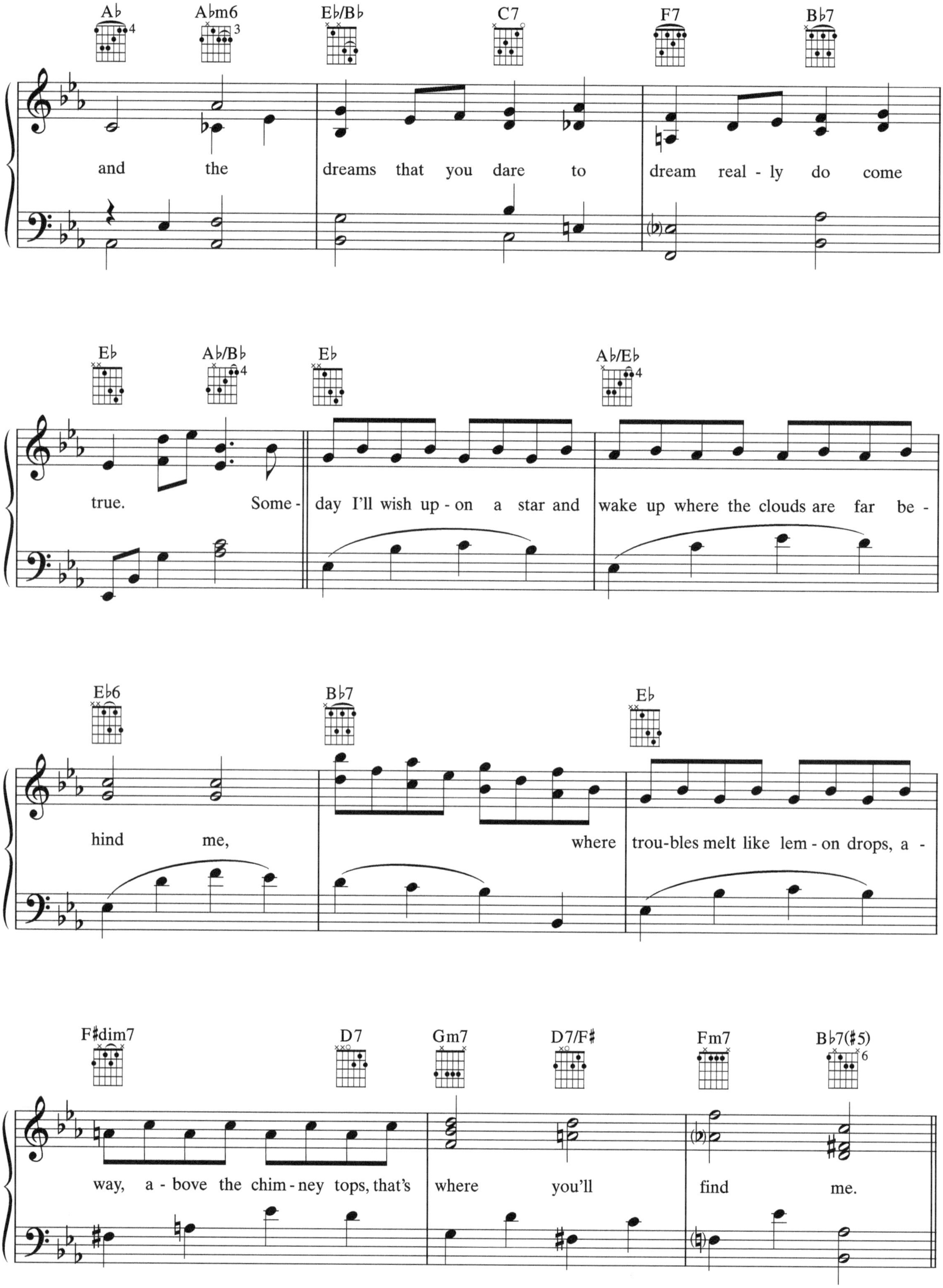
A♭ A♭m6 E♭/B♭ C7 F7 B♭7
and the dreams that you dare to dream real - ly do come
E♭ A♭/B♭ E♭ A♭/E♭
true. Some - day I'll wish up - on a star and wake up where the clouds are far be -
E♭6 B♭7 E♭
hind me, where trou - bles melt like lem - on drops, a -
F♯dim7 D7 Gm7 D7/F♯ Fm7 B♭7(♯5)
way, a - bove the chim - ney tops, that's where you'll find me.

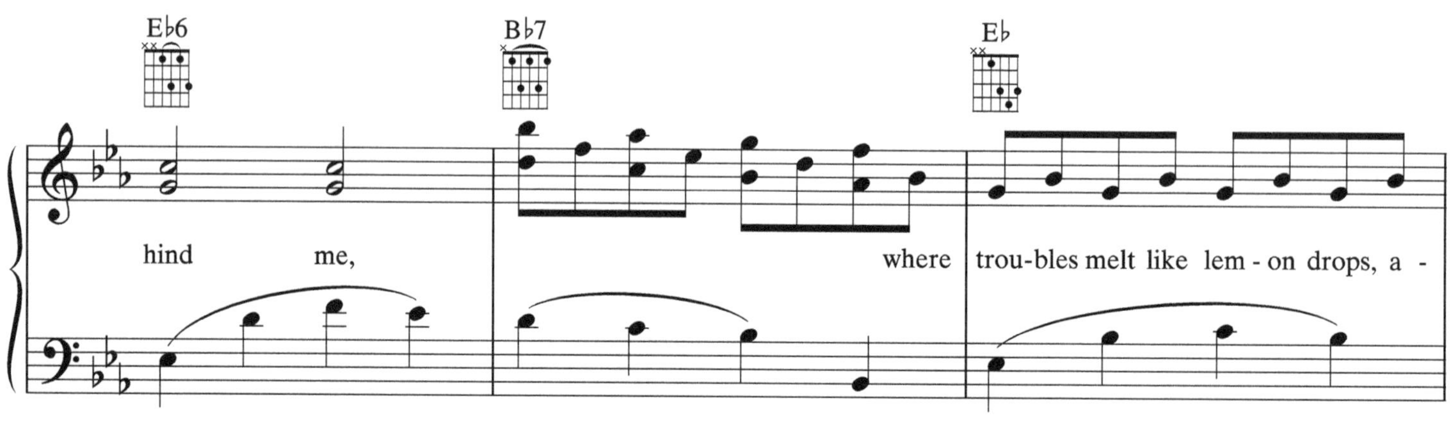

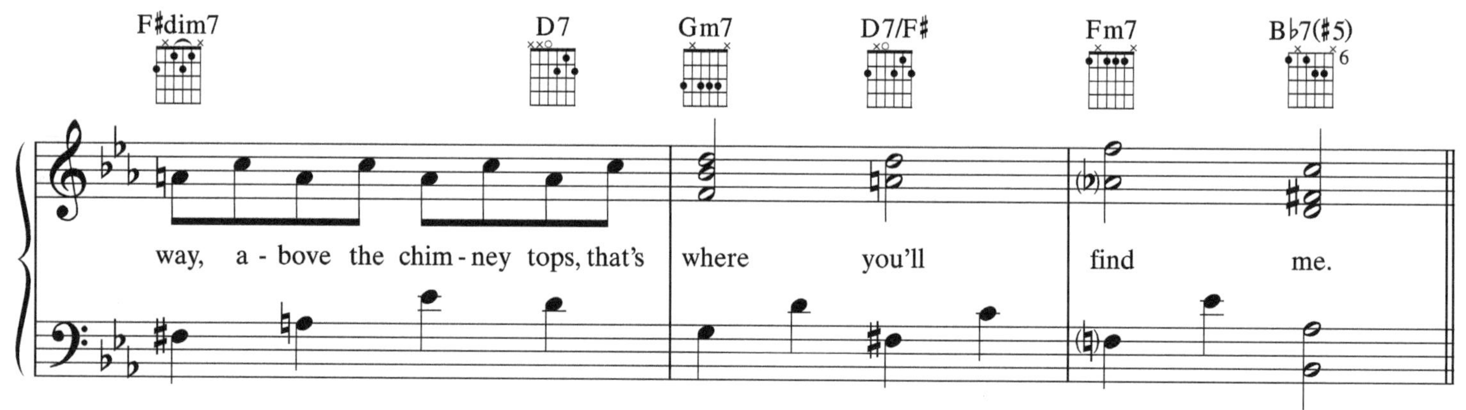

Am7(♭5) D7(♭9) Gm7 C7sus E♭7 A♭ Gm7 C7
Some - where o - ver the rain - bow, blue - birds fly.
A♭ A♭m6 E♭/B♭ C7 F7 B♭7
Birds fly o - ver the rain - bow, why then, oh why can't
1. 2.
E♭ A♭/B♭ E♭ A♭/B♭ E♭
I? I? If hap - py lit - tle blue - birds fly be -
Fm7 B♭7 E♭ E♭maj7
yond the rain - bow, why, oh, why can't I?
molto rit.
pp

THE PINK PANTHER

(from *The Pink Panther*)

By HENRY MANCINI

F7
Em
C7
3
N.C.
Em
3
C
3
1.
Em
3
2.
Em
3
Em(maj7)
p

THE PRAYER

Words and Music by
CAROLE BAYER SAGER and DAVID FOSTER

E♭/F F Gm

know. Let this be our prayer,
are. Let this be our prayer,

C7 A7sus A7

when we lose our way.
when shad - ows fill our day.

Dm B♭ Dm Am B♭ F/C C7

Lead us to a place, guide us with Your grace to a place where we'll be
Help us find a place, guide us with Your grace. Give us faith so we'll be

B♭/F | 1. F | 2. F

safe. 2. I pray we'll find Your | A world where
safe.

Bridge:
B♭
F
B♭
pain and sor-row will be end - ed, and ev - 'ry heart that's bro-ken will be
mf
F
B♭maj7
F
Dm
mend - ed. And we'll re - mem - ber we are all God's chil - dren, reach-ing out to
D♭
B♭m
Fsus
F
touch You, reach-ing to the sky. 3. We ask that You be
Verse 3:
E♭
F7
B♭
f kind, and watch us from a - bove.
B♭(9)/D
E♭
F
We hope each soul will find an - oth - er soul to

A♭/B♭ B♭ Cm
love. Let this be our prayer,
F7 Dsus D7
just like ev - 'ry child who
Gm E♭ Gm Dm E♭ B♭/F F7
needs to find a place, guide us with Your grace. Give us faith so we'll be
mp
E♭/B♭ B♭ Gm E♭ Gm Dm
safe. Needs to find a place, guide us with Your grace.
E♭ B♭/F F7 G♭ A♭ B♭
Give us faith so we'll be safe.
molto rit.

SINGIN' IN THE RAIN

(from *Singin' in the Rain*)

Lyric by
ARTHUR FREED

Music by
NACIO HERB BROWN

G
read - y for love. Let the storm - y clouds chase ev - 'ry
G♯dim7
one from the place. Come on with the rain, I've a
Am7 D7 Am7 D7 Am7 D7 Am7 D7
smile on my face. I'll walk down the lane with a
Am7 D7 Am7 D7
hap - py re - frain, and sing - in', just sing - in' in the
1. 2.
G G♯dim7 Am7 D7 G N.C. G
rain. rain.
3

SOMEWHERE, MY LOVE (LARA'S THEME)

(from *Doctor Zhivago*)

Lyrics by
PAUL FRANCIS WEBSTER

Music by
MAURICE JARRE

Some - where a hill blos - soms in
B♭dim7
D7
Am7
green and gold, and there are
D7
Am7
D7
G
dreams, all that your heart can hold.
C
Some - day we'll meet a -
G
B♭
gain, my love. Some -

F
B♭
day
when - ev - er the spring breaks
D7
G
through.
You'll come to me
B♭dim7
D7
out of the long a - go.
Am7
D7
Am7
Warm as the wind,
soft as the
D7
G
kiss of snow.
'Til then, my
(La - ra, my

B♭dim7
sweet,
own.
think of me now and
D7
Am7
then.
God - speed, my
1.
D7
Am7
D7
G
love,
'til you are mine a - gain.
2.
Am7
D7
'til you are mine
D7(♭9)
G
a - gain,
rit. e dim.

THE SOUND OF SILENCE

Words and Music by
PAUL SIMON

Em
G
D
Em
mains with - in the sound of si - lence.
night and touched the sound of si - lence.
1.
2.
Verse 3:
D
In rest - less dreams I walked a -
3. And in the na - ked light I
saw
mf
Em
C
G
ten thou - sand peo - ple, may - be more.
Peo - ple talk - ing with - out speak - ing,
C
G
C
peo - ple hear - ing with - out lis - t'ning.
Peo - ple writ - ing songs that
G
Em
G
voic - es nev - er share and no one dared dis - turb the

D
Em
sound of si-lence.
4. "Fools," said I, "you do not
Verse 4:
D
Em
know, si-lence like a can-cer grows. Hear my words that I might
C
G
C
G
teach you, take my arms that I might reach you."
C
G
Em
But my words like si-lent rain-drops fell and
G
D
Em
ech-oed in the wells of si-lence.
5. And the peo-ple bowed and

Verse 5:
D
Em
prayed to the ne - on god they made.
C
G
And the sign flashed out its warn - ing in the words that it was
forming.
And the sign said, "The words of the proph - ets are
writ - ten on the sub - way walls and tene - ment halls" and
whis - pered in the sounds of si - lence.
rit. e dim.

THE SUMMER KNOWS

(Theme from *The Summer of '42*)

Lyrics by
ALAN and MARILYN BERGMAN

Music by
MICHEL LEGRAND

C6
C♯m7(♭5)
F♯7(♭9)
Bmaj7
F♯7(♭9)
so she takes her sum - mer time, tells the moon to wait and the
Bmaj7
F7
B♭maj7
F7(♯9)
B♭maj7
E7
A
sun to lin - ger. Twists the world 'round her sum - mer fin - ger, lets you see the
dim.
Am7(♭5)
G/D
Am7(♭5)/D
won - der of it all. And if you've learned your les - son well, there's
mp
a tempo
G/D
Am7(♭5)/D
Gm/D
Am7(♭5)/D
lit - tle more for her to tell. One last ca - ress, it's time to dress for
1.
2.
Gm
Gm
Gm6/9
fall. The fall.

THEME FROM *ICE CASTLES*

(Through the Eyes of Love)

Gm7 Gm7/C Am7 Dm7 Am7 Gm7 Gm7/C
I can see what's mine now, find - ing out what's
Reach - ing out to touch you, I can feel so
Am7 Dm7 B♭maj7 B♭6 A7sus A7 Dm7 G9
true much since I found you look - ing
mf
1.
Gm7 Gm7/C
through the eyes of love. 2. And
2.
Gm7 Gm7/C
through the eyes of
Bridge:
F Dm Am7 Dm
love. And now I do be - lieve that
cresc.
f
Am7 Gm7 C7 F(9) Gm7 Am7
e - ven in the storm we'll find some light. Know - ing you're be -

B♭
G7
Gm7/C
side me I'm all right.
Verse 3:
F(9)
C/F
Cm7/F
3. Please don't let this feel-ing end. It might not come a - gain, and I want to re -
mf
B♭maj7
Am
Gm7
Gm7/C
Am7
Dm7
Am7
mem - ber how it feels to touch you,
Gm7
Gm7/C
Am7
Dm7
B♭maj7
B♭6
A7sus
A7
how I feel so much since I found
Dm7
G9
Gm7
Gm7/C
F
you look - ing through the eyes of love.
rit. e dim.
mp

TALK TO THE ANIMALS

(from *Doctor Doolittle*)

Words and Music by
LESLIE BRICUSSE

G7 Dm B♭/D G Am7
If I could talk to the an - i - mals, learn their
If I spoke slang to o - rang - u - tangs, the ad -
B♭dim7 G/B C Dm7 C/E Dm C
lan - guag - es, may - be take an an - i - mal de - gree.
van - tag - es, an - y fool on earth can plain - ly see.
Dm G C B7
I'd stud - y e - le - phant and ea - gle, buf - fa - lo and
Dis - cuss - ing east - ern art and dra - mas with in - tel - ec - tual
C/B♭ A7 D7 G♯dim7 Am D7 G7sus G7
bea - gle, al - li - ga - tor, gui - nea pig and flea. I could con -
lla - mas. That's a big step for - ward, you'll a - gree. I'd learn to
Gm7 C7 F
verse in po - lar bear and py - thon. And I would
speak in an - te - lope and tur - tle. My Pe - ki -

Gm7 C7sus C7 F
curse in flu - ent kan - ga - roo. If peo - ple
nese would be ex - treme - ly good. If I were
Am D7 G Dm E7
asked me, "Can you speak rhi - noc - er - os?" I'd say, "Of
asked to sing in hip - po - pot - a - mus, I'd say, "Why
Am7 D7 F/G G
cours - er - os. Can't you?" If I con -
not - a - mus?" And would. If I could
Dm B♭/D G Am7 B♭dim7 G/B
ferred with our fur - ry friends, man to an - i - mal,
par - lay with pach - y - derms, it's a fair - y tale
C Dm7 C/E Dm C
think of the a - maz - ing re - par - tee. If I could
wor - thy of Hans An - der - sen or Grimm. The man who

Dm
G
Em
Em7(♭5)
A7
walk with the an - i - mals, talk with the an - i - mals,
walks with the an - i - mals, talks with the an - i - mals,
D7sus
Dm7
E7sus
E7
Am
D7
grunt and squeak and squawk with the an - i - mals,
grunts and squeaks and squawks with the an - i - mals,
Dm
F/G
1.
C
and they could talk to me.
and they can talk to
C/B
C/B♭
A7
If I could
2.
C
B♭/C
me!
Cmaj7
F/C
B/C
C

THEME FROM *NEW YORK, NEW YORK*

Words by
FRED EBB

Music by
JOHN KANDER

F
F7
ver - y heart_ of it; New York,_ New York. I want to
B♭
B♭m
Fmaj7
wake up___ in the cit - y that does - n't sleep and find I'm
Am7
D7
Gm7
C7
king of the hill,__ top of the heap. These lit - tle town
F
Gm7
C7
Gm7
C7
Gm7
C7
blues are melt-ing a - way. I'll make a
F
Cm7
F7
brand - new start__ of it in old New York. If I can

B♭
B♭m
F/C
D7
make it
there, I'll make it
an - y -
where. It's up to
Gm7
Am7
B♭maj7
C7
F
you, New
York, New
York.
Gm7
C7
F
Fmaj7
New York, New
F7
B♭
B♭m
York.
I want to
wake up in the
cit - y that does - n't
Fmaj7
Am7
D7
sleep
and find I'm
"A" Num-ber One,
top of the list,

Slower (♩ = 80)
D♭maj7
C7
Fmaj7
king of the hill,
rit.
"A"Num-ber One.
These lit-tle town
blues
Am7
C7
Fmaj7
Gm7
C7
F
are melt-ing a - way.
I'll make a
brand-new start of it
Cm7
F7
B♭
B♭m
in old New
York.
If I can
make it
there, I'll make it
Tempo I (♩ = 108)
F/C
D7
Gm7
Am7
B♭
B♭/C
an - y -
where. It's up to
accel.
you, New
York, New
F
Gm7
C7
G♭maj7
F
York.
f

THEME FROM *PEYTON PLACE*

Lyrics by
PAUL FRANCIS WEBSTER

Music by
FRANZ WAXMAN

C7
F
Gm7/C
C7
F
That first gen - tle touch of your hands,
B♭/C
F
Gm7
C7
Am7
the look no one else un - der - stands,
Cm7
F7
B♭
B♭dim7
Am7
all these are the things that a love af - fair
G7
B♭m
F/C
Fdim7/C
C7
brings for those who are young and in
1.
F
C7(♭9)
love.
2.
F
love.
rit. e dim.
mp

THEME FROM *ZORBA THE GREEK*

By MIKIS THEODORAKIS

Moderately slow (♩ = 84)

G

mf

Am

G Am D G

1. 2.

A little faster (♩ = 92)

Faster (♩ = 132)
Am
G
Am
D
G
Faster (♩ = 150)

G7
C
G
Am

G
Am
G
Am
G
Am
D
8va

WE BELONG TOGETHER

(from *Toy Story 3*)

Words and Music by
RANDY NEWMAN

G
Em7
Am7
Am7/D
do.
Don't you tell me I'm
not the one;
don't you tell me I ain't no fun.
Just tell me you love me like I love you.
You
G7
C
D
Bm
know you do.
When we're to - geth - er,
gray skies
clear up,
and I
cheer up to where I'm

G
G7sus
G
C
D
less de - pressed.
And sin - cere-ly,
from the
Bm
Em
A7
bot - tom
of my
heart,
I just can't take
D7
Em7
D/F♯
when we're a - part.
Chorus:
G
G/F♯
Em7
G/D
C
C/B
We
be - long
to - geth - er.
D
Em7
D/F♯
G
G7
G7/F
Am7/E
We
be - long
to - geth - er,
yes, we

Am7(♭5)/E♭
G/D
Em
Am7
do.
You'll be
mine
for - ev - er.
D
G
G/F♯
Em7
G/D
C
C/B
We be - long to - geth - er.
D
Em7
D/F♯
G
G7
G7/F
We be - long to - geth -
Am7/E
Am7(♭5)/E♭
G/D
er. You know it's true.
It's gon - na stay this way.
1.
Em
Am7
D7
for - ev - er,
me and you.

Verse 2:
If I could really talk to you, if could find a way.
I'm not shy, there's a whole lot I wanna say. Of course there is.
Talk about friendship and loyalty, talk about how much you mean to me,
And I'd promise to always be by your side whenever you'd need me.
The day I met you was the luckiest day of my life,
And I bet you feel the same, least I hope you do.
So, don't forget me if the future should take you away.
You know you'll always be part of me.
(To Chorus:)

WHAT ARE YOU DOING THE REST OF YOUR LIFE?

(from *The Happy Ending*)

Lyrics by
ALAN and MARILYN BERGMAN

Music by
MICHEL LEGRAND

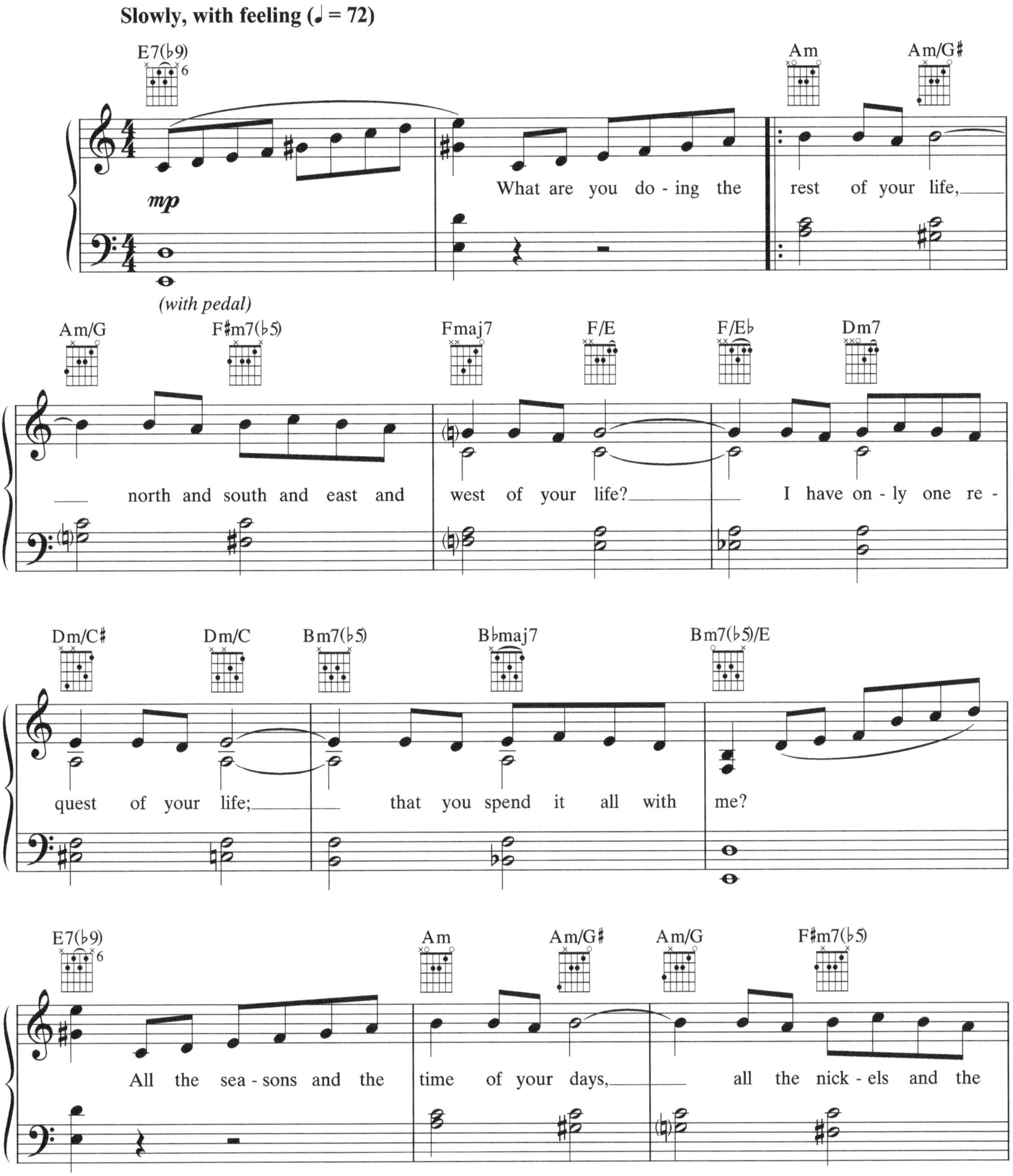

Slowly, with feeling (♩ = 72)
E7(♭9) Am Am/G♯
mp
(with pedal)
What are you do - ing the rest of your life,
Am/G F♯m7(♭5) Fmaj7 F/E F/E♭ Dm7
north and south and east and west of your life? I have on - ly one re -
Dm/C♯ Dm/C Bm7(♭5) B♭maj7 Bm7(♭5)/E
quest of your life; that you spend it all with me?
E7(♭9) Am Am/G♯ Am/G F♯m7(♭5)
All the sea - sons and the time of your days, all the nick - els and the

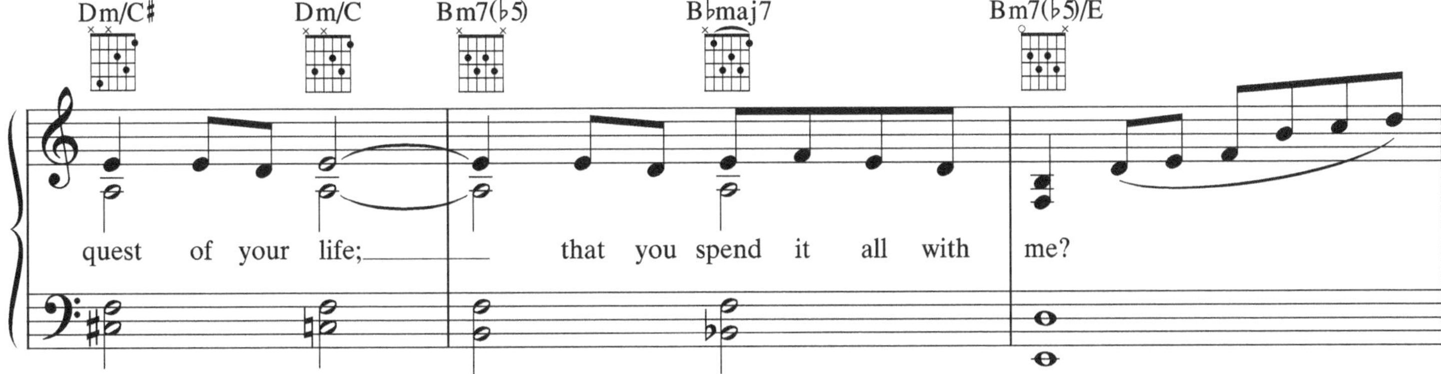

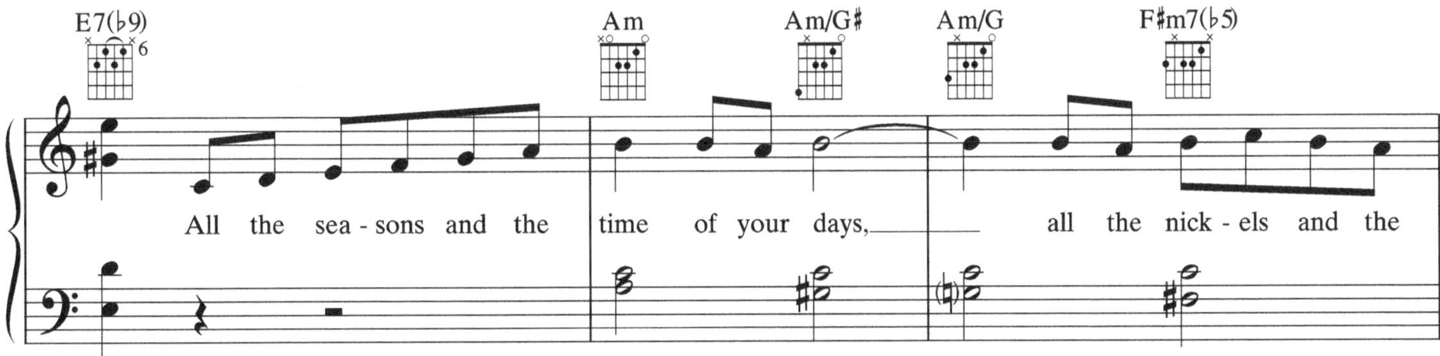

Fmaj7
F/E
F/E♭
Dm7
Dm/C♯
Dm/C
dimes of your days. Let the rea - sons and the rhymes of your days
Bm7(♭5)
E7
Amaj7
all be - gin and end with me. I want to
D/E
E7(♭9)
Amaj7
D/E
E7(♭9)
see your face in ev - 'ry kind of light, in fields of dawn and for - ests of the
Amaj7
A♭m7
D♭7(♭9)
G♭maj7
night. And when you stand be - fore the can - dles on a cake, oh, let me be the
Gm7
C7(♭9)
Fmaj7
Am
Am/G♯
one to hear the si - lent wish you make! Those to - mor - rows wait - ing deep in your eyes,

Am/G
F♯m7(♭5)
Fmaj7
F/E
F/E♭
Dm7
in the world of love you keep in your eyes. I'll a - wak - en what's a -
Dm/C♯
Dm/C
Bm7(♭5)
B♭maj7
Bm7(♭5)/E
sleep in your eyes. It may take a kiss or two!
E7(♭9)
Fmaj7
Bm7(♭5)
E7(♭9)
Through all of my life, sum - mer, win - ter, spring and
Fmaj7
F9(♭5)
Am/E
Bm7/E
E7
fall of my life, all I ev - er will re - call of my life is all of my life with
1.
Am
Bm7(♭5)
E7(♭9)
you! What are you do - ing the
2.
Am
Ddim7
Am
you.

WHAT'S NEW PUSSYCAT?

Words by
HAL DAVID

Music by
BURT BACHARACH

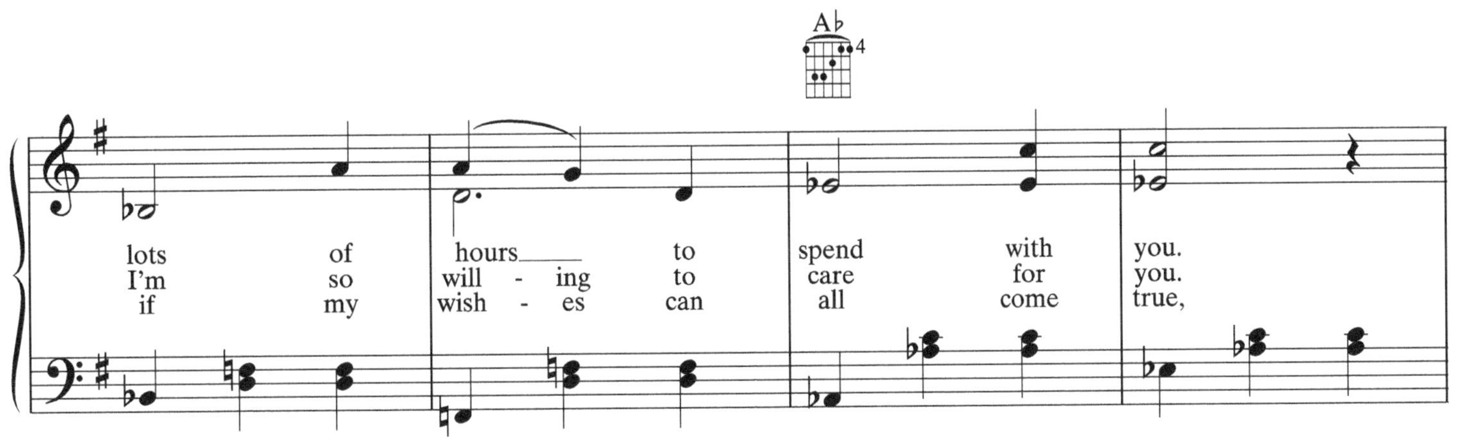
A♭
lots of hours to spend with you.
I'm so will - ing to care for you.
if my wish - es can all come true,

So go and pow - der your cute lit - tle pus - sy - cat nose.
So go and make up your big lit - tle pus - sy - cat eyes.
I'll soon be kiss - ing your sweet lit - tle pus - sy - cat lips.

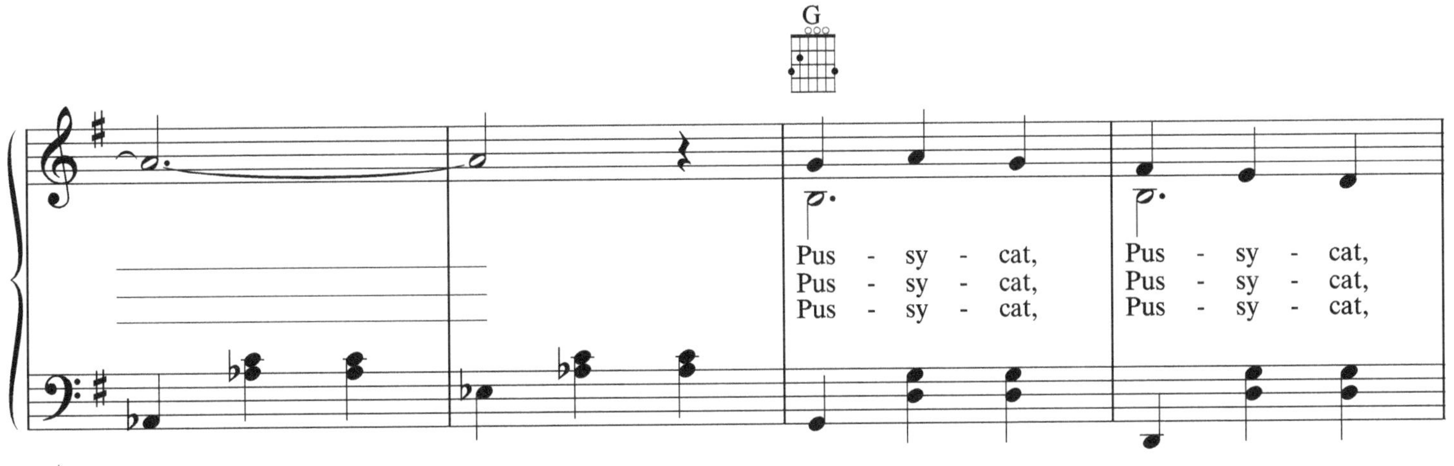
G
Pus - sy - cat, Pus - sy - cat,
Pus - sy - cat, Pus - sy - cat,
Pus - sy - cat, Pus - sy - cat,

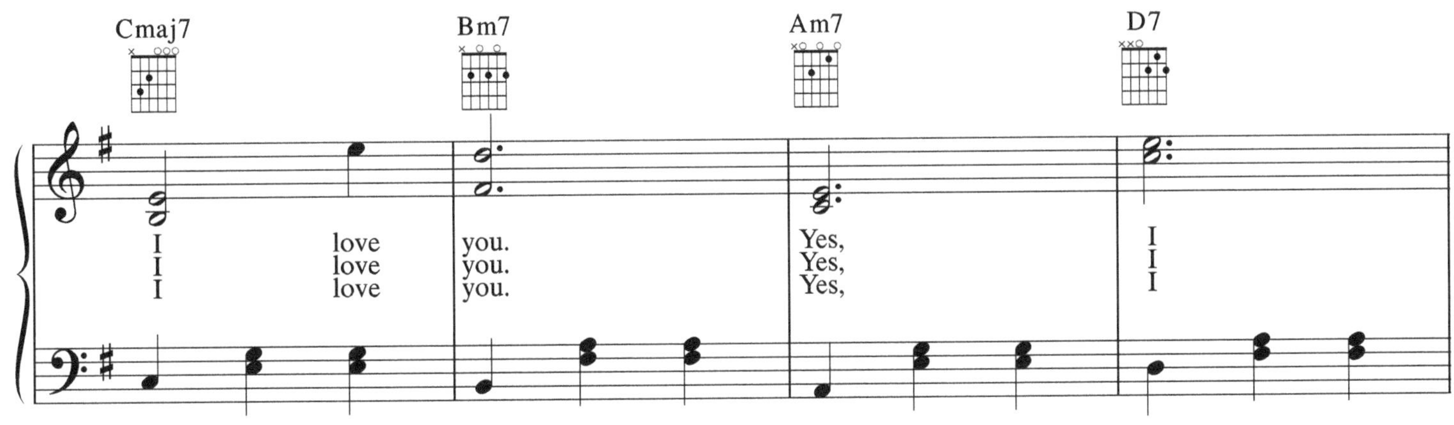
Cmaj7
Bm7
Am7
D7
I love you. Yes, I
I love you. Yes, I
I love you. Yes, I

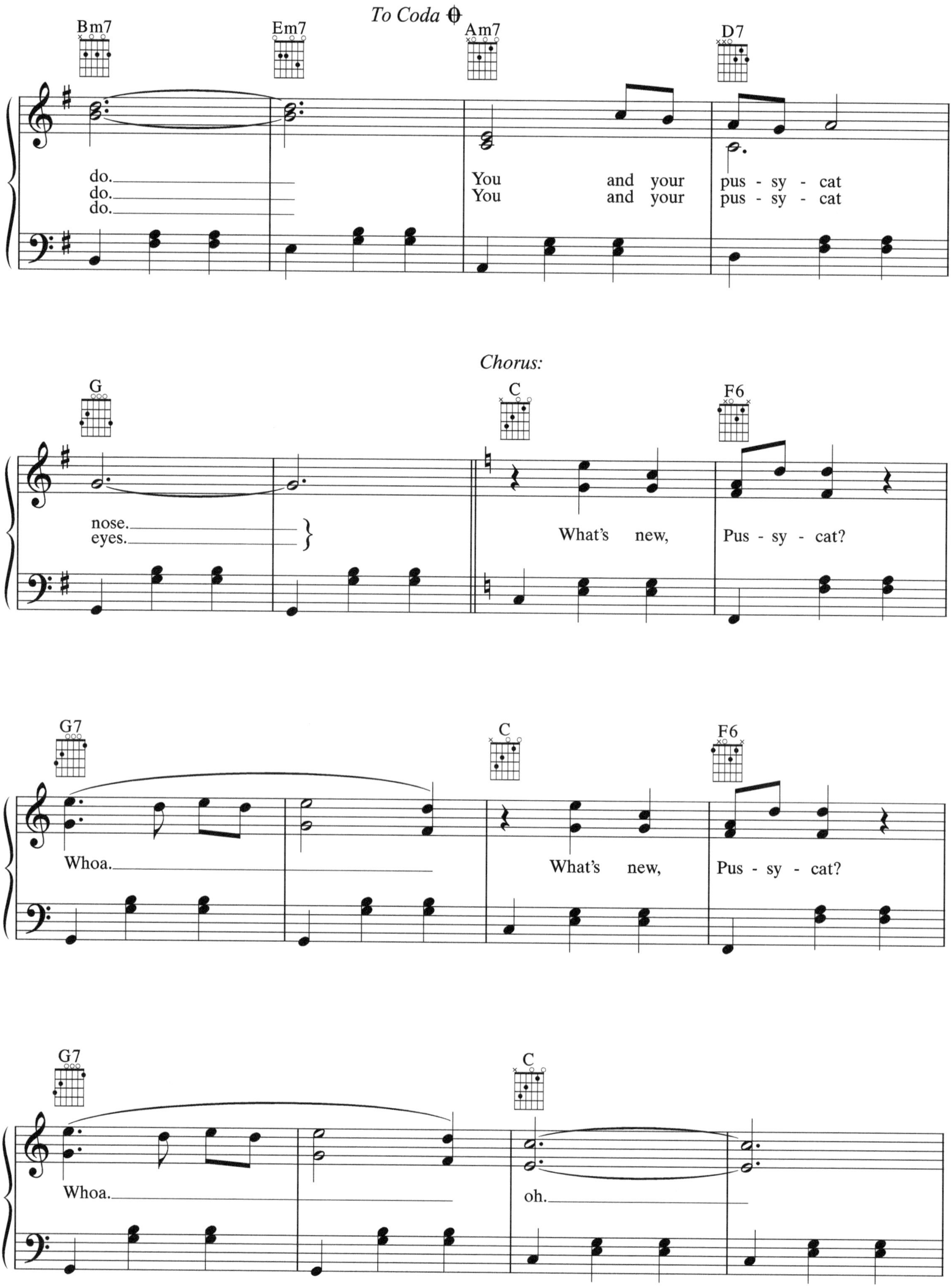

To Coda ⊕

Bm7 Em7 Am7 D7

do.
do.
do.

You and your pus - sy - cat
You and your pus - sy - cat

Chorus:

G C F6

nose.
eyes.

What's new, Pus - sy - cat?

G7 C F6

Whoa.

What's new, Pus - sy - cat?

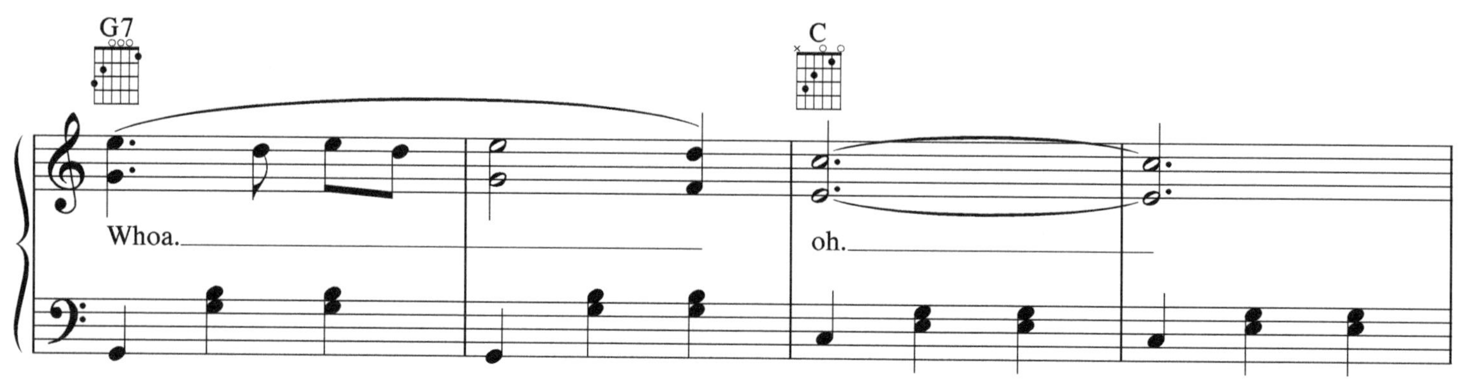

1.
D7
2.
D7
D.S 𝄋 al Coda
𝄌 Coda
Am7
D7
G
You and your pus - sy - cat lips. (Whoa.)
Am7
D7
G
You and your pus - sy - cat eyes. (Whoa.)
Am7
D7
G
You and your pus - sy - cat nose.
poco rit.

YOU'VE GOT A FRIEND IN ME

(from *Toy Story*)

Words and Music by
RANDY NEWMAN

A7
Dm
B♭
E/B
F/C
A/C♯
B♭7
A
Dm
nice warm bed,
you just re - mem - ber what your
old pal said,
boy,
G7
C7
F
D7
G7
C7
you've got a friend in
me.
Yeah,
you've got a friend in me.
1.
F
A7/E
Dm
C♯7
F/C
C7
2.
Bridge:
F
F7
B♭
E
Now some oth - er folks might be a
lit - tle bit smart-er than I am,

F
E7
F6
E
F♯m7
big - ger and strong - er
too.
May - be.
But none of them could
Gdim7
E/G♯
Am
D7
Gm7
C7
C+
ev - er love you the
way I do,
it's
me and you, boy.
Verse 3:
F
C7(♯5)
F7
B♭
Bdim7
3. And as the years go
by,
our
friend - ship will nev - er
F
B♭
Bdim7
F/C
A7/C♯
Dm
die.
You're gon - na see it's our
des - ti - ny.

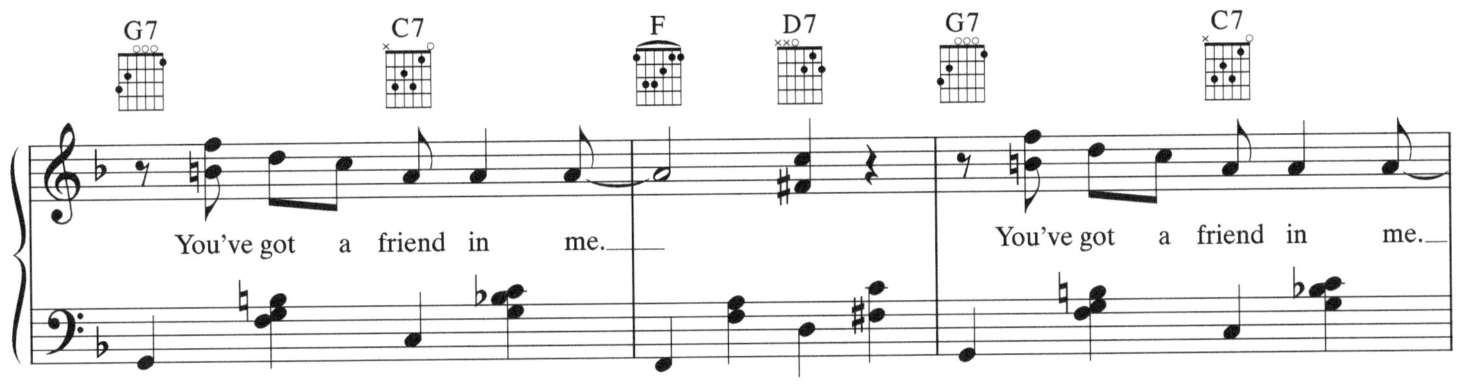

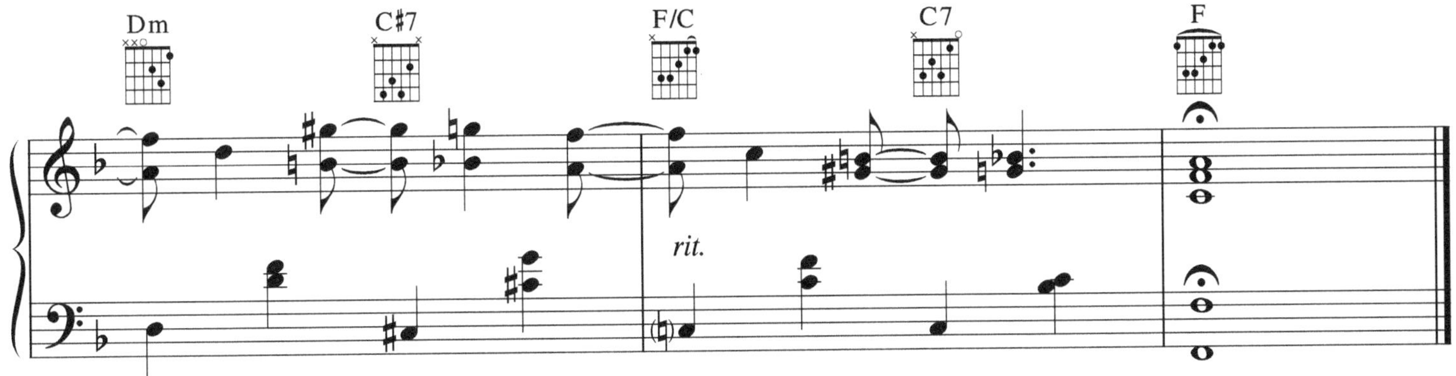

Verse 2:
You've got a friend in me.
You've got a friend in me.
You got troubles, then I got 'em too.
There isn't anything I wouldn't do for you.
If we stick together we can see it through,
'Cause you've got a friend in me.
Yeah, you've got a friend in me.
(To Bridge:)

THE WINDMILLS OF YOUR MIND

(from *The Thomas Crown Affair*)

Words by
ALAN and MARILYN BERGMAN

Music by
MICHEL LEGRAND

Gmaj7
Cmaj7
F♯m7(♭5)
moon, stream, like a clock whose hands are sweep-ing past the min-utes of its face. And the world is like an
B7
B♭dim7
1.
B7
ap-ple whirl-ing si-lent-ly in space, like the cir-cles that you find in the wind-mills of your
dim.
2.
B7
Em
find in the wind-mills of your mind! Keys that jin-gle in your pock-et, words that jin-gle in your
dim.
mp
Am7
D7
Gmaj7
head. Why did sum-mer go so quick-ly? Was it some-thing that you said? Lov-ers walk a-long the
cresc.
mf
G7
Cmaj7
F♯7
shore and leave their foot-prints in the sand. Is the sound of dis-tant drum-ming just the fin-gers of your
cresc.
f

Bm
E7
Am
hand? Pic-tures hang-ing in a hall-way and the frag-ment of a song, half re-mem-bered names of
D7
Gmaj7
Cmaj7
fac-es, but to whom do they be-long? When you knew that it was o-ver, you were sud-den-ly a-
dim.
mf
F♯m7(♭5)
B7
Em
ware that the au-tumn leaves were turn-ing to the col-or of his hair. Like a cir-cle in a
poco a poco rit. e dim.
a tempo
mp
B7
spi-ral, like a wheel with-in a wheel, nev-er end-ing or be-gin-ning on an ev-er spin-ning
B♭dim7
Em/B
B7
Em
reel. As the im-ag-es un-wind, like the cir-cles that you find in the wind-mills of your mind!
rit. e dim.
p
8vb